THE THEORY AND PRACTICE OF DRAWING
IN SI UNITS

A. W. BARNES
C.Eng., M.I.Mech.E.

A. W. TILBROOK
C.Eng., M.I.Mech.E., F.B.H.I.

*Lecturers in the Civil and Mechanical Engineering Department,
The City University. St. John St., London*

THE ENGLISH UNIVERSITIES PRESS LTD
ST. PAUL'S HOUSE   WARWICK LANE
LONDON EC4

First Printed 1962
Second Impression 1966
Third Impression 1968
First (S I) Edition 1970

SBN 340 11463 0 (Case bound edition)
SBN 340 11464 9 (Paper bound edition)

*Printed in Great Britain for The English Universities Press Limited,
by Lowe & Brydone (Printers) Ltd., London*

THE THEORY AND PRACTICE OF DRAWING
IN SI UNITS

THE SCIENCE AND TECHNOLOGY SERIES

General Editor
J. H. CALDERWOOD,
M.Eng., Ph.D., C.Eng., F.I.E.E., F.Inst.P.
*Chairman of the Electrical Engineering Department,
University of Salford*

A Guide to Advanced Electrical Engineering
RUTH V. BUCKLEY,
B.Sc., Ph.D., M.I.E.E.

OTHER BOOKS OF INTEREST

Advanced National Certificate Mathematics
(in two volumes)
J. PEDOE,
M.A., B.Sc.

Engineering Metallurgy
(in two volumes)
RAYMOND A. HIGGINS,
B.Sc. (Birm.), F.I.M.

Higher National Certificate Workshop Technology
T. NUTTALL,
M.I.Mech.E., M.I.Prod.E.

An Introduction to Servomechanisms
F. L. WESTWATER,
O.B.E., M.A. (Edin.), M.A. (Cantab.). M.I.E.E.

and

W. A. WADDELL,
B.Sc., (Glas.), M.I.E.E.

Principles of Engineering Production
A. J. LISSAMAN,
C.Eng., M.I.Mech.E., F.I.Prod.E.

and

S. J. MARTIN,
C.Eng., M.I.Mech.E., M.I.Prod.E.

GENERAL EDITOR'S FOREWORD

This book is concerned with the theory and practice of drawing. It is therefore concerned with a topic which is of vital importance to the engineer. This topic, the importance of which is being increasingly recognised, is that of communication. Drawing is the engineer's special means of communicating his ideas to others; it is the essential link between the creative idea and the working reality.

This does not mean that the engineer will himself be an excellent, or even a good, draughtsman. But it does mean that he must have a working knowledge of the conventions of machine drawing, so that he will be able to look at engineering drawings and know what they mean. He must also be able to sketch out his own plans in such a way that a craftsman can understand clearly what he means to convey, and so that further fruitful and constructive suggestions can be made by both before actual construction commences. Often, of course, a draughtsman will come into the picture as a sort of buffer stage, particularly in large concerns. But frequently in research or development work, especially in light engineering, the engineer will deal directly with the craftsman responsible for building the equipment.

Engineering is developing at an unprecedented rate, and those who are engaged in it may be likened to those venturing into a new and foreign land. It is good that they should know the language.

J. H. CALDERWOOD

FOREWORD

Professor J. C. OAKDEN, M.A., M.Sc. (Tech.), M.I.Mech.E.
Late Head of the Civil and Mechanical Engineering Department,
The City University, St. John St., London

THE authors of this book have for several years been responsible for the teaching of Engineering Drawing in a College having large numbers of students in courses leading to the Engineering Degree of London University and the Diploma in Technology in various branches of engineering and applied science. By experience and experiment they have developed methods which enable them to obtain a high level of efficiency and speed in teaching and which have proved very successful.

In this book, as in their own teaching, they have wisely emphasized the importance of a thorough knowledge of the principles of projective geometry and graphical representation. There is need for a text-book which will assist the student in understanding these fundamentals.

The book should find a wide application in engineering courses of all kinds, and is to be commended to teachers and to students.

PREFACE TO SI EDITION

THE production of a new Metric edition of this book has enabled us to introduce several new problems. We hope that these will prove as useful as the older problems which they replace. In addition the opportunity has been taken to extend the section dealing with Penetrations to include a little known method of solution, utilizing "cutting spheres", for solving certain advanced intersection problems.

The section on Auxiliary Projection has also been expanded to cover "Line and Plane" problems.

In conclusion the authors would like to express their appreciation to Mr. David Oates who has meticulously carried out the onerous task of checking the solutions to all new problems.

A. W. B.
A. W. T.

PREFACE TO FIRST EDITION

THIS book is primarily intended for use in courses leading to University Degrees, Diplomas in Technology, and Membership of the Professional Engineering Institutions. It also represents an attempt on the part of the authors to produce a moderately priced, compact text-book in which the subject is taken to an advanced level. In order to achieve this end certain items, traditionally associated with the subject of engineering drawing, have been omitted where the authors are satisfied that the subject-matter concerned is readily available from other sources. Thus features such as the selection and use of drawing equipment, screw thread forms, screw thread systems, screwed fastenings, locking devices and keys are either omitted entirely or are dealt with in abbreviated form in data sheets at the end of the book. Standard conventions, which are covered in the Abridged Edition of Engineering Drawing Practice (B.S. 308A: 1964), although used throughout the book, have not been reproduced, since it is expected that students will have a copy of these specifications available for reference.

The saving of space effected by these omissions has allowed the remaining sections to be dealt with more completely than is usual in a text-book of this size.

The problem assignments distributed throughout the book are graded and have been selected so that each problem has a "teaching value". With the exception of sketching examples, copywork has been reduced to a minimum. It is our hope that this book will prove to be of value to both lecturers and students of engineering drawing.

The authors are greatly indebted to Dr. W. E. Fisher, O.B.E., D.Sc., for his advice and criticisms during the preparation of the book and to both Dr. J. S. Tait, B.Sc. (Eng.), Ph.D., and Professor J. C. Oakden, M.A., M.Sc.Tech., for their wholehearted support and encouragement.

A. W. B.
A. W. T.

London, 1962.

·CONTENTS

PART I

ENGINEERING DRAWING

Comprising

REPRESENTATION AND SPECIFICATION

Engineering Drawing is a language which expresses itself through the medium of lines instead of words. It enables the Engineer to express his ideas and learn those of others through a system of communication which is truly international. The object of Engineering Drawing is to express ideas, and to impart information, relative to shape, which cannot readily be conveyed in words. By following an agreed system of rules and conventions it is able to do this with a precision adequate for a legal contract, of which engineering drawings may well form a part.

Description of shape must always be achieved through visualization, but before shape can be visualized, it must be REPRESENTED. A drawing represents shape by means of lines and from this representation a visual image is quickly recorded by the brain. This can be seen very clearly by referring to Figs. 1·1, 1·2 and 1·3. A mere glance at each of the figures is sufficient to enable the represented shape to be pictured in the mind. If any of these three figures, simple as they are, were described verbally—i.e. represented by words instead of lines—the description would be involved and the mental images difficult to establish. Drawing is the best method we know of representing shape prior to the physical existence of that shape.

An Engineering Drawing is usually produced with a view to the ultimate manufacture of the object it portrays. With this thought in mind, look again a little more carefully at Figs. 1·1, 1·2 and 1·3 and it will become apparent that these drawings represent the objects in general terms only. We are left with an impression of shape but are given no indication of size and no information regarding the materials from which the objects are made. These drawings, although they represent the objects, do not give sufficient information to enable them to be manufactured.

An Engineering Drawing, suitable for manufacturing purposes, must represent the object so completely and precisely that the REPRESENTATION becomes in fact a SPECIFICATION (see Fig. 1·4).

Summarizing these statements, it can be said that the object of all drawing is visual REPRESENTATION. Representation in its most complete form is SPECIFICATION. Specification is the prime function of a working drawing.

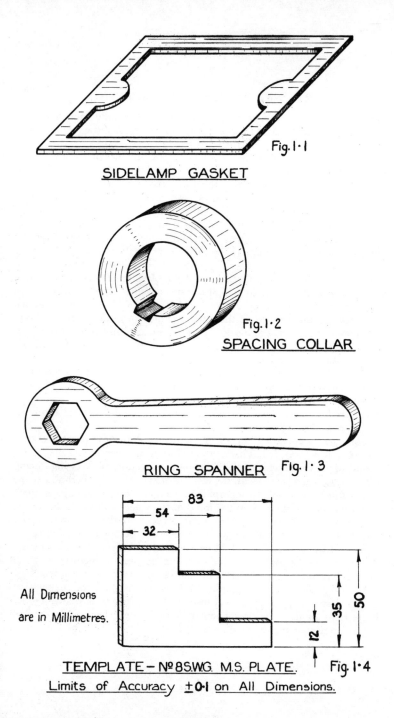

Fig. 1·1

SIDELAMP GASKET

Fig. 1·2

SPACING COLLAR

RING SPANNER   Fig. 1·3

All Dimensions
are in Millimetres.

83

54

32

50

35

12

TEMPLATE – Nº 8 S.W.G. M.S. PLATE.   Fig. 1·4

Limits of Accuracy ±0·1 on All Dimensions.

AN INTRODUCTION TO PROJECTION

Drawings are images projected upon a flat surface (i.e. the drawing paper), and for this reason drawings prepared for technical rather than artistic purposes are generally referred to as PROJECTIONS.

All drawings, because they are projections upon a flat surface, are in fact "two-dimensional" representations of "three-dimensional" objects. Some drawings, however, create the illusion of being "three-dimensional" (see Figs. 1·5, 1·6 and 1·7) and these are known as Pictorial Projections.

Pictorial Projections are dealt with in detail at a later stage. For the present, only a superficial knowledge of them is required. Their value lies in their ability to quickly create a mental image of an object in the mind of the reader. Unfortunately, the image presented is by no means complete. Thus, reference to Figs. 1·5, 1·6 and 1·7 will show that in each of the cases illustrated only three faces of the block are visible; in addition, the depth of the rectangular holes is not specified. In building up his mind-picture of the object, the reader has to assume that the three hidden surfaces are identical with the three visible ones, and that the holes completely penetrate the block. Any attempt to complete the projection by adding dotted lines to indicate hidden edges will reduce its "picture value". Reference to Fig. 1·8 will illustrate this point.

Drawings prepared with a view to the manufacture of parts *must* give *precise* and *complete* information. Except in very simple cases, Pictorial Projection does not meet these requirements, and its use in practice is therefore limited to those occasions where only a quick general appreciation is needed.

For the preparation of manufacturing drawings ORTHOGRAPHIC PROJECTION is preferred. This method of projection represents shape by a series of "two-dimensional" views—the direction of viewing being different for each view—with the result that even the most complex shape can be fully described. Orthographic Projection, although giving complete definition, does not create in the mind of the reader an *immediate* picture of the object. Training and constant practice in the preparation and interpretation of orthographic views is necessary before a mental image of shape can be quickly formed. When dealing with very involved shapes, the orthographic views are sometimes supplemented by pictorial views to assist in creating more quickly a mental image of the main features.

It can be said that Orthographic Projection is used for the preparation of manufacturing drawings because it is specific; and that Pictorial Projections are used mainly for illustrative purposes where only a general representation of shape is required.

Fig. 1·5

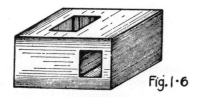

Fig. 1·6

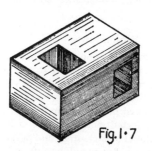

Fig. 1·7

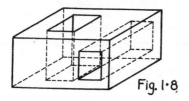

Fig. 1·8

ORTHOGRAPHIC PROJECTION

There are two types of Orthographic Projection in general use; one is known as First Angle and the other as Third Angle Projection. It has already been stated that Orthographic Projections represent an object by means of a series of two-dimensional views—or projections. The difference between First and Third Angle Projections lies in the position of these views relative to each other. Each type will be discussed separately.

First Angle Orthographic Projection

The theory of First Angle Projection will be dealt with by considering two methods of approach:

(1) by moving the object relative to the viewer;
(2) by moving the position of viewing relative to the object.

The first method is that generally adopted by draughtsmen when dealing with the preparation of Engineering Drawings, whereas the second is of use when considering the application of Orthographic Projection to those problems which are usually classified as "Geometrical" and which include, among others, such subjects as Development and Auxiliary Views.

Method 1 (First Angle Projection)

The block from which the projections are to be taken is initially arranged as illustrated at Fig. 1·9, position 1 with "FACE F" parallel to the Plane of Projection, i.e. drawing surface. The direction of viewing is perpendicular to this plane *and remains unaltered throughout all subsequent operations*, the object being always between the viewer and the plane. With the block in position 1, a view is projectedupon the Plane of Projection by means of projectors which are parallel to each other and perpendicular to the plane. For the present this projected view will be referred to as "View X". The block is now rotated about the edge AB through an angle of 90 degrees and is moved to the RIGHT to position 2 and a second view—"View Y"— is projected, views X and Y being in alignment with each other. It will be seen that with the object in position 2 there are certain edges which are not visible to the viewer. These hidden edges are indicated on the projected view by means of dotted lines. Similarly, if the block is rotated about the edge CB through 90 degrees and moved to position 3, the "View Z" can be projected, and this too will be in alignment with "View X".

In the same way, further views could be added to the LEFT of "View X" and also above it. This would, in fact be done if the shape of the object was so complicated that complete description could not be achieved without extra views.

Fig. 1·10 shows the projected views as they would actually appear on the drawing paper, the views X and Y being in horizontal alignment and views X and Z in vertical alignment.

1ST ANGLE PROJECTION
METHOD (I)

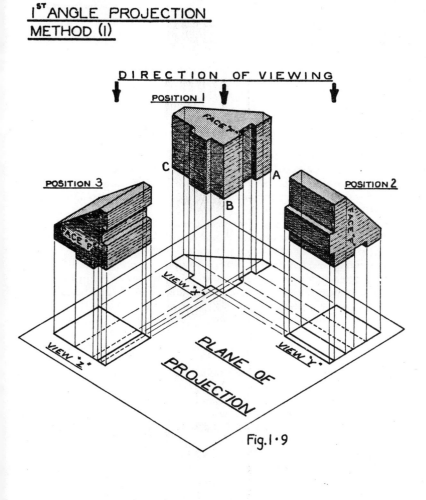

DIRECTION OF VIEWING

POSITION 1

POSITION 3

POSITION 2

FACE "F"

C

A

B

VIEW "X"

VIEW "Z"

VIEW "Y"

PLANE OF PROJECTION

Fig. 1·9

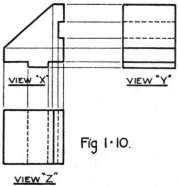

VIEW "X"

VIEW "Y"

VIEW "Z"

Fig 1·10.

METHOD 2. FIRST ANGLE PROJECTION

Three planes of projection, VP. 1, VP. 2 and HP, which are at 90 degrees to each other, are erected as shown at Fig. 1·11 and the object from which the projections are to be taken is suspended between them with FACE F parallel to VP. 1. *The position of the object remains unaltered throughout all subsequent operations.*

Initial viewing is in the direction of the Arrow X perpendicular to VP. 1 and the View X is projected upon this plane by means of projectors which are parallel to each other and normal to the plane.

In a similar fashion View Y can be projected upon the plane VP. 2 by parallel projectors which are normal to this plane—viewing in this case being in the direction of the arrow Y perpendicular to VP. 2. When viewed in this direction, certain edges of the block are not visible to the viewer, and these hidden edges are conventionally indicated on View Y by dotted lines.

When the object is viewed in the direction of the arrow Z—perpendicular to HP—the View Z can be projected upon the Horizontal Plane, the projectors again being parallel to each other and normal to the plane.

If the planes VP. 2 and HP are rabatted as illustrated until they coincide with VP. 1, the three projected views can be shown in one plane and will be positioned relative to each other as indicated in chain-dotted lines at Fig. 1·11.

Because the object was stationary during projection, the views X and Y will be in horizontal alignment and views X and Z will be in vertical alignment. This can be seen more clearly in Fig. 1·12, which shows the projected views as they would appear on the drawing paper.

1ST ANGLE PROJECTION
METHOD (2)

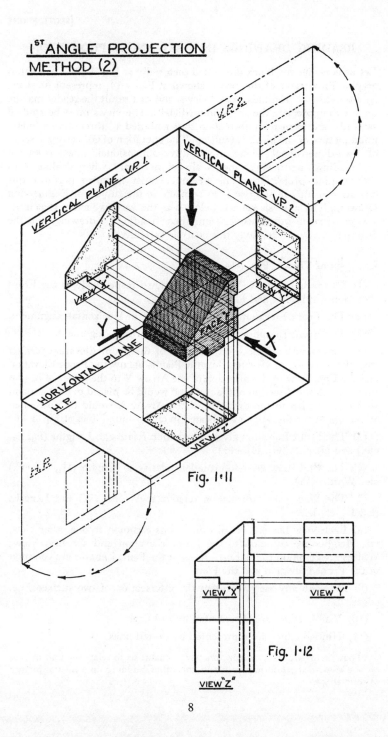

Fig. 1·11

Fig. 1·12

READING DRAWINGS IN FIRST ANGLE PROJECTION

Let us consider the block illustrated pictorially at Fig. 1·13. The Orthographic Projections of this block, shown at Fig. 1·14, represent its shape by a series of "two-dimensional" views, and as a result the reader may be unable to appreciate the shape immediately. The views must be studied carefully and from the information thus gathered a "three-dimensional" mind picture of the block is built up. The operation of converting a series of "two-dimensional" views into a "three-dimensional" image is known as "reading" a drawing, and is always necessary when dealing with orthographic projections. The beginner must learn to perform this operation readily if progress is to be made in the subject of Engineering Drawing. The analysis set out below lists the various factors that must always be taken into consideration when "reading" a drawing, and the beginner is advised to study this analysis carefully.

Analysis of Views (Fig. 1·14)

(1) The three views X, Y and Z are known respectively as the Front Elevation, End View and Plan.

*(2) The Front Elevation and End View are in Horizontal Alignment.

*(3) The Front Elevation and Plan are in Vertical Alignment.

(4) The views are placed on that side of the Front Elevation *furthest from* the direction of viewing, thus the Plan is BELOW the Front Elevation and the End View in the direction of the Arrow Y to the RIGHT of it. (An End View in the direction of the Arrow P would be placed to the LEFT and an Inverted Plan in the direction of the Arrow A would be positioned ABOVE the Front Elevation as indicated in chain-dotted lines at Fig. 1·14.)

(5) The Front Elevation gives information relative to Lengths (L_1, L_2, etc.) and Heights (H_1, H_2, etc.)

(6) The End View gives information relative to Heights (H_1, H_2, etc.) and Widths (W).

(7) The Plan gives information relative to Widths (W) and Lengths (L_1, L_2, etc.).

*(8) Each view has one set of dimensions common to one other view, viz. Heights are common to the Front Elevation and the End View; Widths are common to the End View and the Plan; Lengths are common to the Front Elevation and the Plan.

(9) Lines on any view represent the intersection of two surfaces, i.e. edges.

(10) Visible edges are represented by full lines.

(11) Hidden edges are represented by dotted lines.

*These items are the prime factors which enable us to relate the information on one view to the information on another, thus building up a mental picture of solid shape.

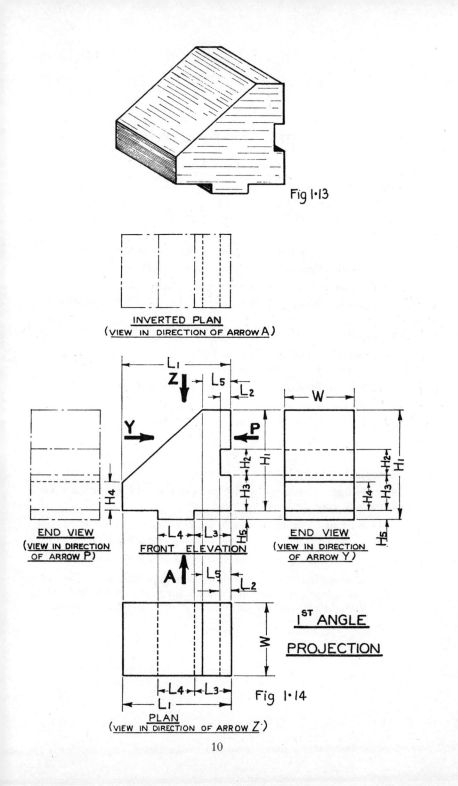

Fig 1·13

INVERTED PLAN
(VIEW IN DIRECTION OF ARROW A)

END VIEW
(VIEW IN DIRECTION
OF ARROW P)

FRONT ELEVATION

END VIEW
(VIEW IN DIRECTION
OF ARROW Y)

1ST ANGLE

PROJECTION

Fig 1·14

PLAN
(VIEW IN DIRECTION OF ARROW Z)

10

FIRST ANGLE PROJECTION

Problems and Solutions

Example 1

A block is illustrated pictorially at Fig. 1·15. Do not reproduce this view, but draw instead, in First Angle Orthographic Projection, the following views:

(1) A Front Elevation looking in the direction of the Arrow X.

(2) An End View looking in the direction of the Arrow Y.

(3) A Plan looking in the direction of the Arrow Z.

Solution. See Fig. 1·16.

Example 2

A machine Cross Slide is shown at Fig. 1·17. Do not copy this view, but draw, in First Angle Projection:

(1) A Front Elevation looking in the direction of the Arrow X.

(2) An End View looking in the direction of the Arrow Y.

(3) A Plan looking in the direction of the Arrow Z.

Solution. See Fig. 1·18.

Example 3

A single-throw Crankshaft is illustrated at Fig. 1·19. Using First Angle Projection, draw the following views:

(1) A Front Elevation looking in the direction of the Arrow X.

(2) An End View looking in the direction of the Arrow Y.

(3) A Plan looking in the direction of the Arrow Z.

Solution. See Fig. 1·20. This solution introduces the projection of cylinders. It should be noted that when dealing with cylindrical parts, *the centre lines of those parts are shown on all views in which they appear.*

11

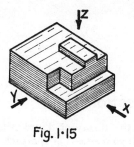

Fig. 1·15

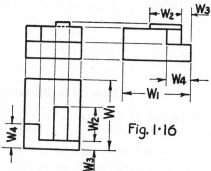

Fig. 1·16

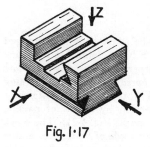

Fig. 1·17

Fig. 1·18

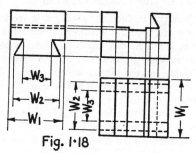

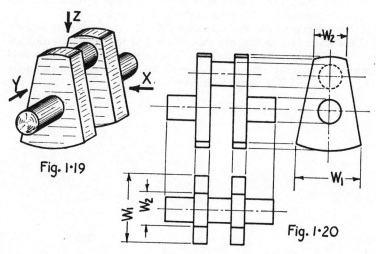

Fig. 1·19

Fig. 1·20

THIRD ANGLE PROJECTION

As in the case of First Angle Projection, the theory of Third Angle Projection will be dealt with by considering two methods of approach:

(1) By moving the object relative to the viewer.

(2) By moving the viewing position relative to the object.

Method 1 (Third Angle Projection)

The block from which the projections are to be taken is initially arranged as shown at Fig. 1·21, position 1—the FACE F being parallel to the plane of projection. The direction of viewing is perpendicular to this plane *and remains unaltered throughout all subsequent operations*, the object being always between the viewer and the plane. With the block in position 1 a view is projected upon the Plane of Projection by means of parallel projectors perpendicular to the plane (see View X, Fig. 1·21). The block is now rotated about the edge AB through an angle of 90 degrees and is then moved to the LEFT to position 2. With the block in its new position a second view—View Y—is projected, views X and Y being in alignment with each other. (The dotted lines shown on View Y represent those edges of the block which are not visible to the viewer.)

If the object is rotated about the edge CB and is then moved to position 3, View Z can be projected and this, too, will be in alignment with View X. Fig. 1·22 shows the arrangement of the projected views as they would appear on the drawing paper with views X and Y in horizontal alignment and views X and Z in vertical alignment.

13

3RD ANGLE PROJECTION.
METHOD (1)

DIRECTION OF VIEWING

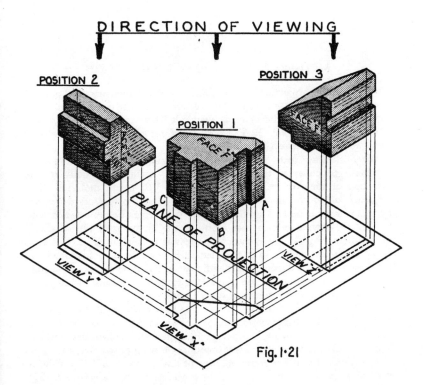

Fig. 1·21

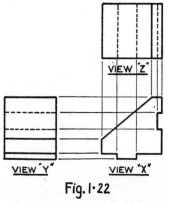

Fig. 1·22

METHOD 2. THIRD ANGLE PROJECTION

Three planes of projection, VP. 1, VP. 2 and HP, which are at 90 degrees to each other, are erected as illustrated at Fig. 1·23. The object from which the projections are to be taken is suspended between these planes with FACE F parallel to VP. 1. *The position of the object remains unaltered throughout all subsequent operations.*

When dealing with Third Angle Projection by this method it is necessary to consider transparent Planes. Viewing is initially in the direction of the Arrow X perpendicular to VP. 1 and the View X is *projected back* on to this plane by means of parallel projectors which are normal to the plane. In a similar manner View Y can be *projected back* on to VP. 2—viewing in this case being in the direction of the Arrow Y perpendicular to VP. 2—by parallel projectors normal to VP. 2. The view Z can be *projected back* on to the plane HP when the object is viewed in the direction of the Arrow Z perpendicular to HP. The parallel projectors in this case are normal to the plane HP. Hidden edges are indicated on the projected views by means of dotted lines.

If the planes VP. 2 and HP are rabatted as shown until they coincide with VP. 1, the three views can be shown in one plane and will be positioned relative to each other as indicated in chain-dotted lines at Fig. 1·23. Because the object was stationary during projection, the views X and Y will be in horizontal alignment and views X and Z will be in vertical alignment. This can be seen more clearly by reference to Fig. 1·24, which shows the projected views as they would appear on the drawing paper.

3RD ANGLE PROJECTION
METHOD (2)

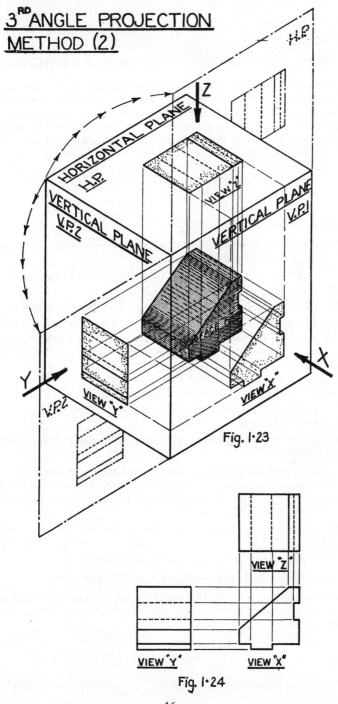

Fig. 1·23

VIEW "Z"

VIEW "Y"   VIEW "X"

Fig. 1·24

16

READING DRAWINGS IN THIRD ANGLE PROJECTION

The various factors that must be taken into consideration when reading Third Angle Projections are the same as those that have to be considered when interpreting First Angle Projections; there is, however, one difference—the position of the views relative to the Front Elevation. In Third Angle Projection the views are always placed on the side of the Front Elevation *adjacent to* the direction of viewing (see Fig. 1·26).

With the exception of Item 4, the analysis of views set out below is exactly as for First Angle Projection and the analysis is merely repeated in full for the convenience of the reader.

Analysis of Views (Fig. 1·26)

(1) The three views X, Y and Z are known respectively as the Front Elevation, End View and Plan.

*(2) The Front Elevation and the End View are in Horizontal Alignment.

*(3) The Front Elevation and the Plan are in Vertical Alignment.

(4) The views are placed on that side of the Front Elevation *adjacent to* the direction of viewing, the Plan is ABOVE the Front Elevation and the End View in the direction of the Arrow Y to the LEFT of it. (An End View in the direction of the Arrow P would be placed to the RIGHT, and an Inverted Plan BELOW the Front Elevation gives information relative to Lengths (L_1, L_2, etc.) and Heights (H_1, H_2, etc.)

(6) The End View gives information relative to Lengths (L_1, L_2, etc.) and Widths (W).

(7) The Plan gives information relative to Widths (W) and Lengths (L_1, L_2, etc.).

*(8) Each view has one set of dimensions common to one other view, viz. Heights are common to Front Elevation and the End View; Widths are common to the End View and Plan; Lengths are common to the Front Elevation and Plan.

(9) Lines on any view represent the intersection of two surfaces, i.e. edges.

(10) Visible edges are represented by full lines.

(11) Hidden edges are represented by dotted lines.

* These items are the prime factors which enable us to relate the information on one view to the information on another, thus building up a mental picture of solid shape.

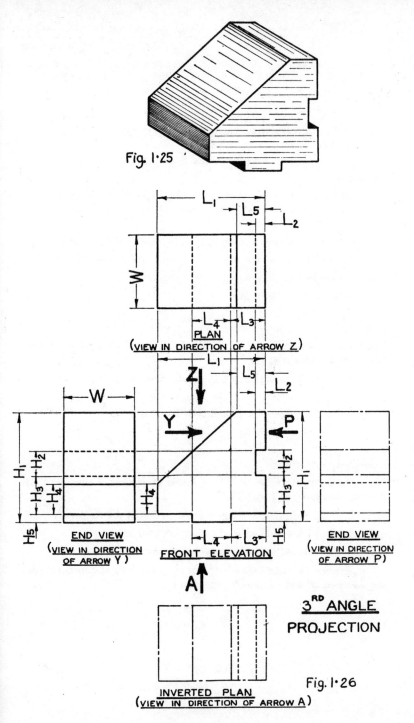

Fig. 1·25

L₁ L₅ L₂

W

L₄ L₃

PLAN
(VIEW IN DIRECTION OF ARROW Z)

L₁ L₅ L₂

Z

W

Y

P

H₁ H₂

H₃ H₄

H₅ END VIEW
(VIEW IN DIRECTION OF ARROW Y)

FRONT ELEVATION

A

L₄ L₃

H₃ H₂

H₅ END VIEW
(VIEW IN DIRECTION OF ARROW P)

H₁

3ᴿᴰ ANGLE
PROJECTION

INVERTED PLAN
(VIEW IN DIRECTION OF ARROW A)

Fig. 1·26

18

THIRD ANGLE PROJECTION

Problems and Solutions

Example 1

A Floor Stand is illustrated pictorially at Fig. 1·27. Do not reproduce this view, but draw instead, in Third Angle Orthographic Projection, the following views:

(1) A Front Elevation looking in the direction of the Arrow X.

(2) An End View looking in the direction of the Arrow Y.

(3) A Plan looking in the direction of the Arrow Z.

   Solution. See Fig. 1·28.

Example 2

Draw the following views, in Third Angle Projection, of the Clamp illustrated pictorially at Fig. 1·29:

(1) A Front Elevation looking in the direction of the Arrow X.

(2) An End View looking in the direction of the Arrow Y.

(3) A Plan looking in the direction of the Arrow Z.

   Solution. See Fig. 1·30.

Example 3

Draw the following views in Third Angle Projection of the Dead Eye Bearing illustrated at Fig. 1·31:

(1) A Front Elevation looking in the direction of the Arrow X.

(2) An End View looking in the direction of the Arrow Y.

(3) A Plan looking in the direction of the Arrow Z.

   Solution. See Fig. 1·32. *Note that the centre lines of cylindrical parts are shown on all views in which they appear.*

19

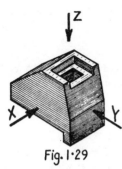

Fig.1·27

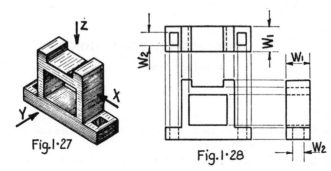

Fig.1·28

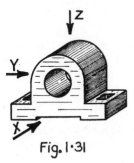

Fig.1·29

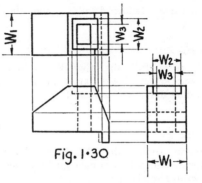

Fig.1·30

Fig.1·31

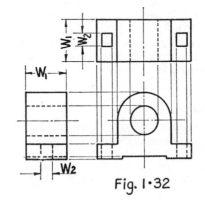

Fig.1·32

ORTHOGRAPHIC PROJECTION
Problem Assignments

Exercise 1

Draw in First or Third Angle Projection the following views of the Block illustrated pictorially at Fig. 1·33:

    (1) A Front Elevation looking in the direction of the Arrow A.

    (2) An End View looking in the direction of the Arrow B.

    (3) A Plan looking in the direction of the Arrow C.

Do not insert hidden detail, but state the angle of projection used.

Exercise 2

Examine carefully the other Blocks illustrated at Figs. 1·33A to 1·33K and state which Blocks have a Front Elevation identical with the Front Elevation drawn in Exercise 1.

Exercise 3

Examine carefully the other Blocks illustrated at Figs. 1·33A to 1·33K and state which Blocks have an End View identical with the End View drawn in Exercise 1.

Exercise 4

Examine carefully the other Blocks illustrated at Figs. 1·33A to 1·33K and state which Blocks have a Plan identical with the Plan drawn in Exercise 1.

Exercise 5

State which, if any, of the Blocks have all Three Views identical with those drawn in Exercise 1.

NOTE: The prime dimensions of the Blocks shown in Figs. 1·33A to 1·33K are the same as for Fig. 1·33.

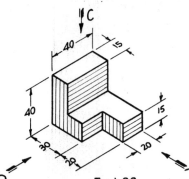

Fig. 1·33

Fig. 1·33 A

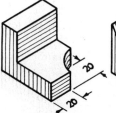

Fig. 1·33 B

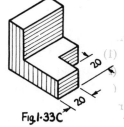

Fig. 1·33 C

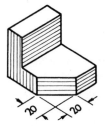

Fig. 1·33 D

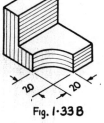

Fig. 1·33 E

Fig. 1·33 F

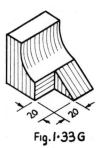

Fig. 1·33 G

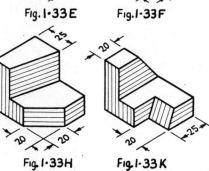

Fig. 1·33 H

Fig. 1·33 K

ALL DIMENSIONS IN MMS.

ORTHOGRAPHIC PROJECTION
Problem Assignments

Exercise 6

Draw FULL SIZE and in First or Third Angle Projection the following views of the Block illustrated pictorially in Fig. 1·34:

(1) A Front Elevation looking in the direction of the Arrow X.

(2) An End View looking in the direction of the Arrow Y.

(3) A Plan looking in the direction of the Arrow Z.

In this drawing hidden detail is not required and the dimensions should not be shown. State the type of orthographic projection used.

Exercise 7

Draw FULL SIZE and in First or Third Angle Projection the following views of the Block illustrated pictorially in Fig. 1·34A:

(1) A Front Elevation looking in the direction of the Arrow X.

(2) An End View looking in the direction of the Arrow Y.

(3) A Plan looking in the direction of the Arrow Z.

Show hidden detail in the Front Elevation, View (1). No dimensions are required, but the type of orthographic projection used must be stated.

NOTES: The above problems are designed to teach linework and orthographic projection and the solutions which consist entirely of straight lines are easily lined in.

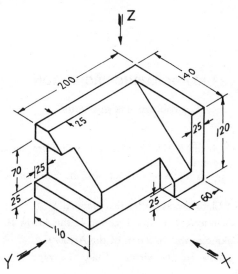

Fig. 1·34
ALL DIMENSIONS IN MM'S.

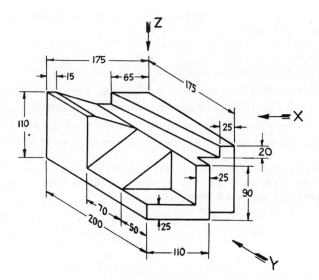

Fig. 1·34 A
ALL DIMENSIONS IN MM'S.

24

ORTHOGRAPHIC PROJECTION

Problem Assignments

Exercise 8

The Front Elevation and End View of a Supporting Bracket are shown in First Angle Projection in Fig. 1·35.

Draw the following views FULL SIZE and in First or Third Angle Projection:

(1) The Front Elevation as given, i.e. View A.

(2) An End View looking in the direction of the Arrow B.

(3) A Plan looking in the direction of the Arrow C.

Insert hidden details on ALL views. State the type of orthographic projection used.

Exercise 9

The Front Elevation and Plan of a Girder Clip are illustrated in Fig. 1·36, the views being First Angle Projections.

Draw to a scale 2/1 the following views in First or Third Angle Projection:

(1) The Front Elevation given, i.e. View A.

(2) An End View looking in the direction of the Arrow B.

(3) An End View looking in the direction of the Arrow C.

(4) An Inverted Plan looking in the direction of the Arrow D.

Insert hidden detail on ALL views, and state the type of projection used.

NOTES: The above problems are progressively harder to solve than those that precede them and it is important to fully interpret the given views before the solution is attempted.

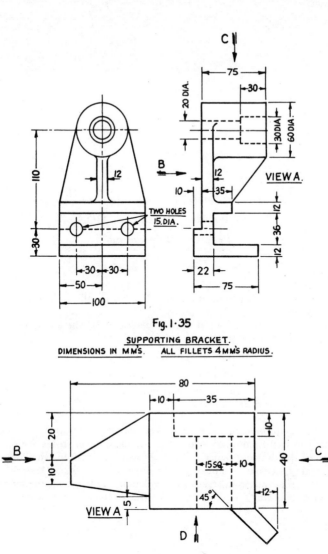

Fig. 1·35

SUPPORTING BRACKET.
DIMENSIONS IN MM'S. ALL FILLETS 4 MM'S RADIUS.

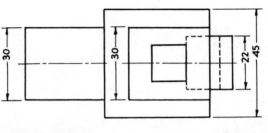

GIRDER CLIP.
ALL DIMENSIONS IN MM'S.

Fig. 1·36

26

ORTHOGRAPHIC PROJECTION

Problem Assignments

Exercise 10

An Elevation and End View of a Guide Bracket are shown in First Angle Projection in Fig. 1·37.

Do not copy these views but draw to a scale of 3/1 the following views in First Angle Projection

(1) A Front Elevation looking in the direction of the Arrow B.

(2) An End View to be positioned on the LEFT of the New Elevation.

(3) An Inverted Plan to be positioned ABOVE the New Elevation. Insert hidden detail in ALL views.

NOTES: When producing a drawing to a scale that is not normally included on the Standard Engineers' Scale, it is advisable to construct one on the bottom of the drawing paper and to use this rather than to calculate each individual dimension. There are two reasons for this: (1) it is not prone to errors due to mistakes in calculation; (2) if left on the finished drawing it is useful for reference. (A map furnishes a good example of this.)

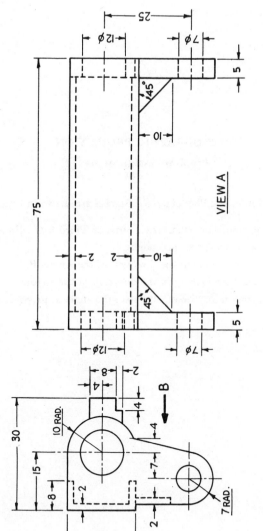

Fig. 1·37

GUIDE BRACKET.
ALL DIMENSIONS IN MMS.

28

ORTHOGRAPHIC PROJECTION

Problem Assignments

Exercise 11

The Front Elevation and Plan of a Feed Bracket are shown in First Angle Projection in Fig. 1·38.

Draw the following views FULL SIZE in First or Third Angle Projection:

(1) The Elevation as shown in View A.

(2) An End View looking in the direction of the Arrow B.

(3) An Inverted Plan looking in the direction of the Arrow C.

Insert hidden detail in ALL views, and state the angle of projection used.

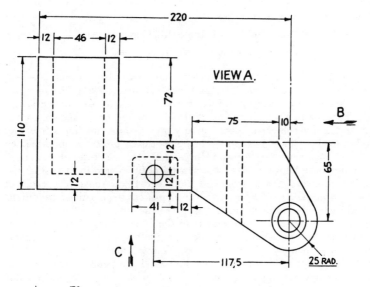

VIEW A.

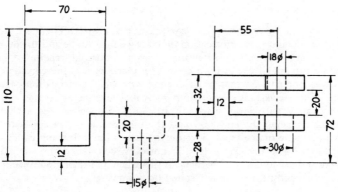

DISCUSSION ON FIRST AND THIRD ANGLE PROJECTIONS

Although the theory of First and Third Angle Orthographic Projections has been dealt with in detail in the preceding pages, there are two questions concerning these methods of projection which the student may want to ask at this stage. They are:

(1) Why are First and Third Angle Projections so named?

(2) Which is the best of the two methods to use?

Question 1 has a simple answer—consider two planes which intersect at right angles to form four quadrants as illustrated at Fig. 1·39. Following standard mathematical procedure, the four quadrants are known as the First, Second, Third and Fourth Angles in the order shown on the diagram. If an object is placed in any one of these quadrants (see Fig. 1·40), the orthographic views of the object can be projected upon the two intersecting planes (Vertical and Horizontal) which comprise the quadrant. It is important to note that the viewing positions are fixed so that the object is *always* viewed from the Right and from Above *irrespective of the quadrant in which the projection is carried out.* Under these conditions an object projected in the First quadrant is in First Angle Projection and if placed in the Third quadrant is in the Third Angle Projection. It is apparent that there must also be two further types of orthographic projection—namely Second Angle and Fourth Angle, but a little thought will show that neither of these two projections are "pure", i.e. each gives one view in First Angle and one in Third Angle projection, and for this reason they are not considered to be standard projections.

Question 2 is by no means an easy question to answer. There are two schools of thought—one advocating the use of Third Angle and the other of First Angle projection. After many years' industrial experience involving a prolonged use of both types of projection, it is the considered opinion of the authors that when dealing with small and medium sized orthographic views, neither method has any real advantage over the other. When dealing with large views, Third Angle Projection has a slight advantage. Placing the end view and the plan of the object adjacent to the viewed side of the front elevation renders a large drawing easier to read. First Angle Projection is still, however, considered the standard method in this country, and because of this when Third Angle Projection is used this fact must be clearly stated on a drawing.

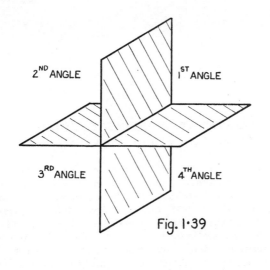

2ND ANGLE

1ST ANGLE

3RD ANGLE

4TH ANGLE

Fig. 1·39

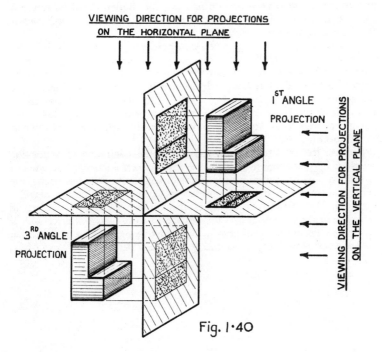

VIEWING DIRECTION FOR PROJECTIONS
ON THE HORIZONTAL PLANE

1ST ANGLE
PROJECTION

VIEWING DIRECTION FOR PROJECTIONS
ON THE VERTICAL PLANE

3RD ANGLE
PROJECTION

Fig. 1·40

THE TREATMENT OF HIDDEN DETAIL ON
ORTHOGRAPHIC VIEWS

When describing shape by means of orthographic views, two types of line are generally used—full lines to depict visible edges and dotted lines to denote detail which is not visible. It is a basic rule of projection that whenever detail is VISIBLE it MUST ALWAYS be drawn in irrespective of the fact that it may have been previously indicated on other views. There is, however, *no such rule appertaining to HIDDEN DETAIL.* In practice, it is left to the discretion of the draughtsman to insert as much as he thinks necessary for a clear and correct interpretation of the drawing. A good draughtsman will concentrate on *inserting* the hidden detail wherever it appears *and will only omit it when, in his opinion, its insertion will confuse the drawing and render it difficult to interpret.*

The beginner, lacking the necessary experience, usually finds difficulty in arriving at an intelligent decision, and sometimes decides to omit hidden detail because its insertion would involve him in extra work. This practice is to be deplored, since it frequently results in the object being inadequately described (see Fig. 1·41). Some beginners always insert every bit of hidden detail on all views regardless of the fact that by so doing they may be producing a confused drawing which is very difficult to interpret (see Fig. 1·42).

Because the student lacks experience at the beginning of a drawing course it is customary to give precise instructions regarding the amount of hidden detail required on the problem solutions. This has been done here, and on the first set of problem assignments *all* hidden detail is required. On subsequent examples the student is asked to insert all *necessary* hidden detail and is then expected to use his initiative and, if unsure, to discuss the problems with his instructor, bearing in mind that *hidden detail should only be omitted if it confuses the drawing.*

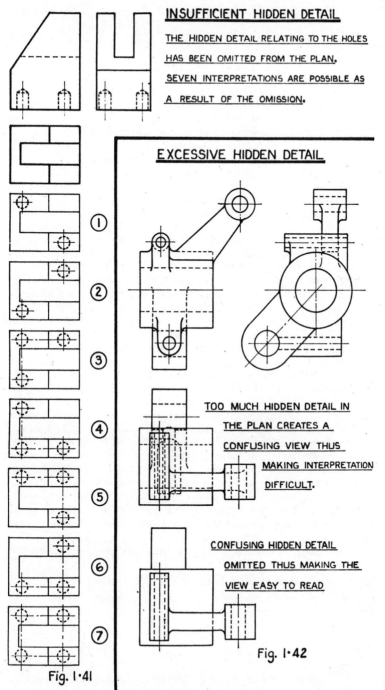

INSUFFICIENT HIDDEN DETAIL

THE HIDDEN DETAIL RELATING TO THE HOLES
HAS BEEN OMITTED FROM THE PLAN.
SEVEN INTERPRETATIONS ARE POSSIBLE AS
A RESULT OF THE OMISSION.

EXCESSIVE HIDDEN DETAIL

TOO MUCH HIDDEN DETAIL IN
THE PLAN CREATES A
CONFUSING VIEW THUS
MAKING INTERPRETATION
DIFFICULT.

CONFUSING HIDDEN DETAIL
OMITTED THUS MAKING THE
VIEW EASY TO READ

Fig. 1·42

Fig. 1·41

34

CHOICE AND NUMBER OF VIEWS

We have seen that every drawing is a representation of shape and, when it is fully dimensioned, the information it gives must be a complete specification. This implies something more than the mere statement of all necessary manufacturing data; it is also essential that the drawing illustrates every detail feature of shape in a way that cannot be misunderstood. A written statement must be clear, concise and without any ambiguity, and equally this alternative method of description must pass the same tests. This criterion should be kept constantly in mind.

In Fig. 1·43 two First Angle orthographic views of a piece of shafting are given, an elevation with a plan beneath it, and as the object is symmetrical about a longitudinal axis, a centre line is shown in both views. It is not apparent from the drawing that the object is cylindrical and therefore these views are not the best choice. An elevation and end view of the shaft are shown in Fig. 1·44; these two views give a clear and immediate idea of shape, and consequently they are the most satisfactory views to reproduce. With a cylindrical object it can be said that when the dimensions are given there will be no doubt of the shape involved, but this argument is not really sound—the views, *by themselves*, should be clear and precise as they are in Fig. 1·44.

In Fig. 1·45 the elevation and plan of a rectangular block are given, the views being First Angle projections. One surface of the object has been labelled with the letter "A" in both views. Although this surface has been correctly illustrated in the two views, the drawing is not complete because the shape of surface "A" is not shown. In Fig. 1·46 a third view has been added, an end view projected to the right-hand (R.H.) side of the elevation: this view clearly illustrates the shape of surface "A", which in this instance happens to be a curved surface of radius "R". The surface could have anyone of an infinite variety of shapes *without the plan and elevation being changed in any way*—views (A), (B) and (C) in Fig. 1·47 being a selection of three of them—and it will therefore be obvious that the end view must be given. In this particular case where the shape is very simple it may be considered reasonable to omit the plan if the two elevations are given, but it should be noted that, in general, it is desirable to draw all three views.

Summarizing, the above examples underline two very important features in Engineering Drawing:

(1) thought must be given to the choice of views; and

(2) it is generally necessary to draw three orthographic views.

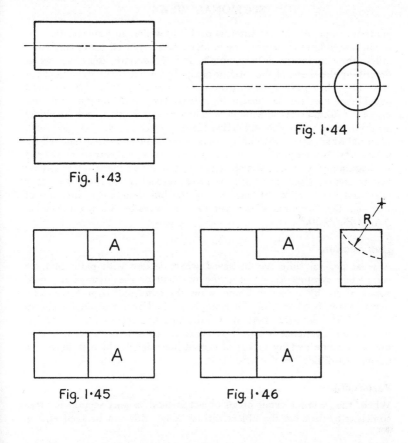

Fig. 1·44

Fig. 1·43

Fig. 1·45   Fig. 1·46

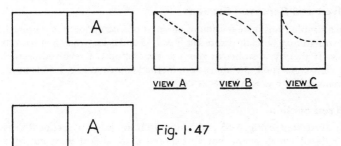

VIEW A   VIEW B   VIEW C

Fig. 1·47

36

SECTIONAL VIEWS

When a component has an Internal profile as well as an External one, the use of dotted lines to portray the hidden edges may well prove confusing unless the component is very simple. It is customary, therefore, when describing the shape of the interior of an object to imagine the object cut away in such a fashion as to expose the internal profile. The exposed detail being therefore visible can be indicated on the drawing by full lines instead of dotted ones. Such a view is known as a Section, and the object is said to have been cut by a Section Plane—see Figs. 1·48, 1·49 and 1·50. Material which is actually cut by the Section Plane is crossed-hatched by means of thin lines at 45 degrees. It is necessary to indicate on one of the Orthographic views the position of the Section Plane which is lettered for easy reference. The type of line used to signify a Section Plane is a heavy chain-dot line—arrows at each end of the line denote the direction of viewing. The Sectional View itself should always be titled, e.g. Section AA, at Fig. 1·50.*

Half Section

A great deal of time can be saved when dealing with parts that are completely symmetrical by drawing one half of the view as it would appear if cut by a Section Plane, while the other half is portrayed as a normal view of the exterior. An example of a half Sectional View is shown at Fig. 1·51—note the method of indicating the Section Plane and the title of the Sectional View. It is generally considered unnecessary to portray on one half by means of dotted lines detail which is shown by means of full lines on the other half.

Part Sections

Where the internal detail of an object is local, a part section is often sufficient to describe the object satisfactorily—this can be seen at Fig. 1·52.

Revolved and Removed Sections

Where a simple transverse section of one part of a component is required, the treatment may be as illustrated at Fig. 1·53 and is known as a REVOLVED SECTION. If there is insufficient room to superimpose a revolved section on the view concerned, the alternative method shown at Fig. 1·54 is used, and this is called a REMOVED SECTION.

Staggered Section

This is illustrated at Fig. 1·55 and is used to bring into the sectional view interior detail which would not be exposed if the object were cut by a single section plane.

* When the section plane coincides with the main centre line of the view the section plane is sometimes omitted and the sectional view is not then named.

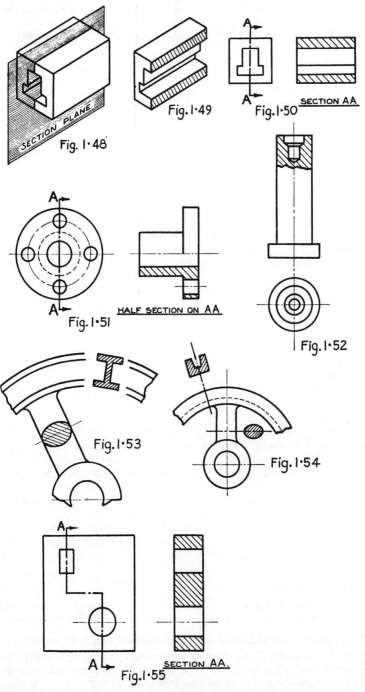

Fig. 1·48

SECTION PLANE

Fig. 1·49

Fig. 1·50

SECTION AA

Fig. 1·51

HALF SECTION ON AA

Fig. 1·52

Fig. 1·53

Fig. 1·54

Fig. 1·55

SECTION AA.

D

38

CONVENTIONS APPERTAINING TO SECTIONAL VIEWS

Treatment for different Materials cut by Section Planes

The modern method, as recommended in B.S.S. 308, is to indicate the cut surface of ALL METALS by thin section lines set at 45 degrees as illustrated at *a*, Fig. 1·56. Materials other than metals are depicted by various means and those most commonly met with in engineering practice are shown at *b*, *c*, *d* and *e*, Fig. 1·56.

Treatment for different Components cut by the same Section Plane

Fig. 1·57 shows a typical case of an assembly drawing where several components are cut by the Section Plane. Each part must have a distinctive form of sectioning in order that the separate components may be easily picked out when reading the drawing. Where the separate parts are metal, as is usually the case in engineering work, the section lines must all be full lines set at 45 degrees and a distinction is made by varying the spacing between the section lines and by reversing the 45 degrees angle. Intelligently used, this method is quite satisfactory and a large number of components can be clearly portrayed. It should not be necessary to alter the angle of the section lines or to substitute a different type of line.

Treatment of Webs

When a web is cut longitudinally by a Section Plane it is customary to leave the web unsectioned (see Fig. 1·58). It must be borne in mind that a web is usually thin with respect to the overall thickness of the main body, and if the web were sectioned a false conception of solidity is given (see Fig. 1·59). A web cut transversely, however, is sectioned in the usual way as shown at Fig. 1·60.

Components not sectioned when cut by a Section Plane

If any solid component of well-known form is cut longitudinally by a Section Plane, it is conventional to leave these parts unsectioned, since they have no internal profile to reveal, and sectioning is considered a waste of time. Standard hexagonal and square nuts are also treated in this way because they are more easily recognized on a drawing by their distinctive external profile. A list of components not sectioned is as follows: solid shafts, bolts, screws, studs, rivets, keys, cotters, wheel spokes, standard nuts. It should be noted that this convention holds if the parts are sectioned longitudinally; it does *not* apply if the section is transverse (see Fig. 1·61 and 1·62).

Treatment of Dimensions

When dimensions are shown on the face of a section, the section lines must be broken to avoid cutting across the figures (see Fig. 1·63).

Treatment of Components cut by more than one Section Plane

Fig. 1·64 illustrates how, when two sectional views of an assembly are required, the *spacing and direction* of the section lines remains the same for each component on both sectional views.

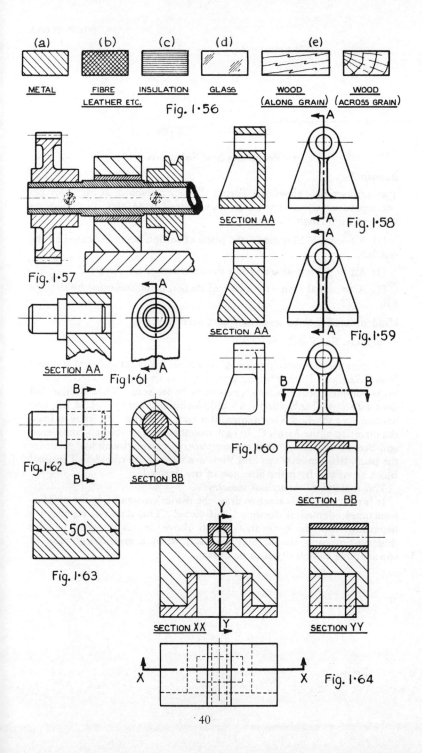

(a) METAL
(b) FIBRE LEATHER ETC.
(c) INSULATION
(d) GLASS
(e) WOOD (ALONG GRAIN)   WOOD (ACROSS GRAIN)

Fig. 1·56

Fig. 1·57

SECTION AA   Fig. 1·58

SECTION AA

SECTION AA   Fig.1·61

Fig. 1·62   SECTION BB

SECTION AA   Fig.1·59

Fig. 1·60

SECTION BB

Fig. 1·63   50

SECTION XX

SECTION YY

Fig. 1·64

SECTIONAL VIEWS

Problems and Solutions

Exercise 1

Two orthographic views of a Terminal Block are shown at Fig. 1·65. Do not reproduce these views, but draw instead, FULL SIZE, the following views in First Angle Projection:

(1) A Sectional Elevation—the plane of section being indicated by the line AA.

(2) An End View as seen from the direction of the Arrow C.

(3) A Sectional Plan—the plane of section being indicated by the l.ne BB.

Hidden detail is to be inserted where necessary.

Solution. See Fig. 1·66.

Readers are *particularly requested to note the treatment of a view projected from a Sectional View.* The cut-away object is always considered restored to its complete shape before a new view is projected. Thus Section BB does *not* show what Section AA would look like if cut by a plane BB, and neither does the End View represent a view of Section AA as seen from the direction of the Arrow C. In each case the *complete* object is considered and Section BB shows what the *complete object* would look like if cut by the plane BB: similarly the End View is a view of the complete Terminal Block as viewed from the direction of the Arrow C.

This is standard throughout industry.

It is relevant at this stage to draw the reader's attention to the practice sometimes adopted of drawing "half-views". This does not represent a departure from the convention stated above, but is intended to save drafting-time and should only be used when a *symmetrical* view of considerable complexity is to be drawn.

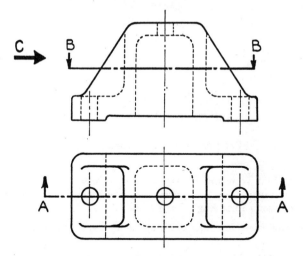

Fig. 1·65

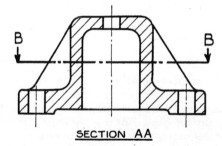

SECTION AA

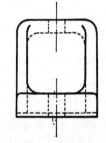

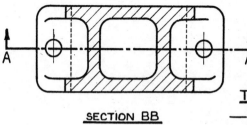

SECTION BB

Fig. 1·66

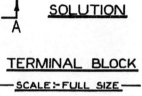

SOLUTION

TERMINAL BLOCK

── SCALE :- FULL SIZE ──

SECTIONAL VIEWS

Problems and Solutions

Exercise 2

The Elevation, End View and Plan of a Junction Box are illustrated at Fig. 1·67. Do not reproduce these views, but draw instead, FULL SIZE, the following views using First Angle Projection:

(1) A Sectional Elevation—the plane of section being indicated by the line BB.

(2) A Sectional End View—the plane of section being indicated by the line AA.

(3) A Sectional Plan—the plane of section being represented by the line CC.

Insert hidden detail where necessary.

Solution. See Fig. 1·68.

Attention is drawn to the treatment of the central rib (or partition) when cut by the Section Planes BB and CC. The rib is treated as a web and when cut transversely (by the plane CC) it is sectioned in the usual way, but when cut longitudinally (by the plane BB) it is conventionally left unsectioned. The reasons for this convention are dealt with earlier in this book, under the heading of Conventions Appertaining to Sectional Views.

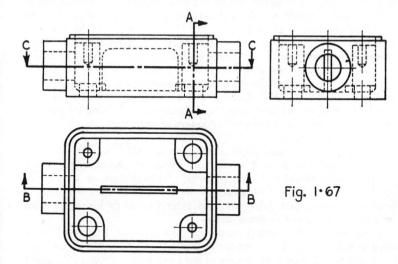

A

C ←   → C

A

B ←   → B

Fig. 1·67

A

C ←   SECTION BB   → C

A

SECTION AA

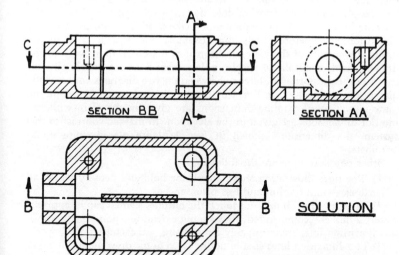

B ←   → B

SOLUTION

SECTION CC

JUNCTION BOX
—SCALE:- ½ FULL SIZE.—

Fig. 1·68

44

DIMENSIONS

It has been previously stated in the book that Engineering Drawing has to follow an agreed system of rules and conventions, with a precision adequate for a legal contract of which Engineering Drawings may well form a part. The statement is repeated here because it sets the pattern that has been universally adopted for dimensioning a drawing; dimensions must follow accepted rules, be precise and, above all, be perfectly clear. The details of this pattern are satisfactorily dealt with by the recommendations outlined in B.S. 308 and B.S. 308.A, and the student is advised to read these very carefully, especially while attempting to dimension a drawing for the first time. In addition, it is considered necessary to emphasize certain features that are often overlooked.

Many students regard dimensioning as a rather tedious and unimportant addition to a drawing and often, in consequence, insert dimensions hurriedly and unintelligently. This attitude, if adopted in practice, could well be disastrous, but in any circumstance will tend to produce a drawing that is difficult to interpret. Considerable thought must be given to the layout of dimensions.

Compare the two drawings on the facing page, Figs. 1·69 and 1·70. A notable difference is at once apparent; in Fig. 1·69 *none* of the dimensions have been placed within the outline of any view, while in Fig. 1·70 most of them are within the outline. The treatment shown in Fig. 1·69 is correct because the added information does not interfere with, or obscure, the drawing itself—i.e. the presentation of shape is as clear and precise after dimensioning as before. Thus, dimensions should in general be placed round the outside of the views and form, as it were, a framework to the drawing, with none placed within, unless there is no reasonable alternative. Another important difference between the two diagrams concerns the dimensions themselves. In Fig. 1·69 related dimensions are placed on the same view, i.e. all exterior dimensions are given in the plan, while all interior dimensions are given in the elevation. In marked contrast to this system, the dimensions shown in Fig. 1·70 are placed quite indiscriminately.

Other points to note are the following:

(1) The lines illustrating shape should be bold and densely black; all other lines should be thin and less pronounced.

(2) "Limit" lines should not touch the outline, a small gap of approximately 2 mm is recommended; they should extend to a point just beyond the dimension line, approximately 5 mm being satisfactory.

(3) The dimension lines should not be close to the drawing outline, the minimum allowance that is in common use being 6 mm to 9 mm.

(4) The division line of a fractional dimension should be horizontal (or in an equivalent position).

(5) All dimensions should be readable from the bottom right-hand corner of the drawing.

(6) Dimensions having been inserted on one view must not be repeated on another.

(7) Dimensions must not be positioned in such a way that centre lines or outlines cut through them.

45

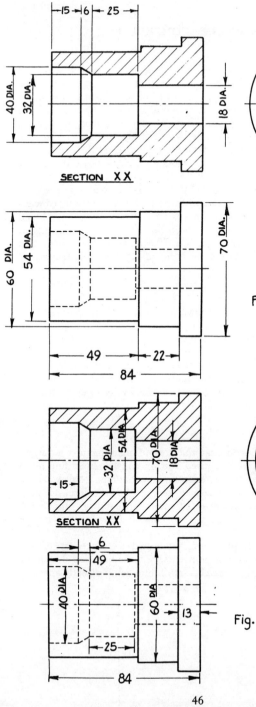

SECTION XX

60 DIA.
54 DIA.
70 DIA.
15 6 25
40 DIA.
32 DIA.
18 DIA.
49 22
84

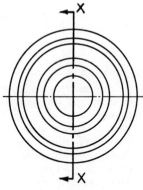

X
X
CORRECT

Fig. 1·69

X
X
INCORRECT

Fig. 1·70

SECTION XX
15
32 DIA.
54 DIA.
70 DIA.
18 DIA.
6
49
40 DIA.
60 DIA.
13
25
84

DIMENSIONAL CONTROL 1

Tolerances

When a drawing reaches the workshops, those concerned with the manufacture of the parts should know precisely how accurate the finished work must be. A machined part, for instance, may have to fit within another very closely indeed, while the external surfaces of a large casting may perhaps vary as much as 6 mm from the stated dimensions without causing any trouble whatsoever. The permissible variation in size—*the allowable tolerance*—is therefore of vital importance, and the drawing, in addition to specifying shape and size, should clearly indicate the degree of accuracy required.

It should be noted that sometimes position is of greater importance than size, or a geometrical feature such as straightness, flatness, concentricity, roundness or parallelism requires special consideration. In all cases the degree or type of control should be stated on the drawing, as described with considerable detail in B.S. 308 (and also B.S. 1916), and it will therefore be sufficient to discuss here only the essential features of dimensional control.

Limits

A typical dimensioned drawing is shown in Fig. 1·71; it is assumed that, in this particular case, the allowable tolerance on all dimensions is 0·2 mm—i.e. that the finished machined part will pass inspection providing no dimension is more than 0·1 mm greater than the stated size, or more than 0·1 mm less than the stated size. The maximum and minimum sizes are known as the "limits" or "limiting dimensions". Where all dimensions can be given the same tolerance, it is better to state this in a general note, as shown in Fig. 1·72.

Application

It is important to understand that the cost of manufacture is largely dependent upon the accuracy required and, in consequence, fine limits must never be demanded when quite wide variations in size can be allowed. This feature is emphasized in Fig. 1·73, where, to meet functional requirement or the need of interchangeability, only a few surfaces are given small tolerances, the remaining dimensions have a tolerance of $\pm0\cdot1$ mm.

Three different methods of stating individual tolerances are shown in B.S. 308, but, as it should not be necessary to deduce one dimension from another, Method A is preferred, both limits being directly specified as shown in Fig. 1·74.

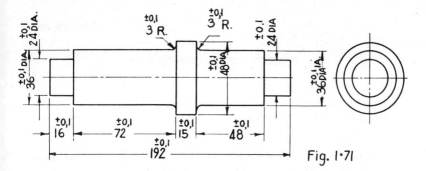

Fig. 1·71

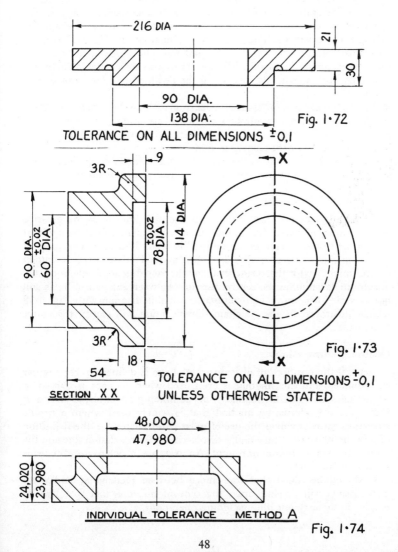

TOLERANCE ON ALL DIMENSIONS ±0,1

Fig. 1·72

SECTION X X

TOLERANCE ON ALL DIMENSIONS ±0,1
UNLESS OTHERWISE STATED

Fig. 1·73

INDIVIDUAL TOLERANCE   METHOD A

Fig. 1·74

DIMENSIONAL CONTROL 2

Datum Surface, etc.

Functional dimensions, i.e. dimensions which directly affect the use or application of a machine part, should be clearly stated on a drawing, and this will necessitate the selection of a datum surface, line or point from which to set off these dimensions. In general, this reference will be a machined surface where symmetry does not exist, or a centre line where the object is of symmetrical form. It must be noted that the choice of datum is inevitably linked with a process of manufacture, or with the order or sequence in which the surfaces or other features of shape are brought into existence. The cast bracket illustrated in Fig. 1·75 emphasizes this feature; after casting, the first machining operation would be the preparation of the surface AB in order to provide a suitable datum for "marking out" and finally inspecting the position of the various drilled holes.

Fig. 1·76 illustrates an alternative example where the centre line AB is the datum, and here it should be recognized that although the dimensions are not "set off" from the axis of symmetry, they must be interpreted as being symmetrical with respect to AB.

In Fig. 1·77 the datum is the point A, i.e. the centre of the large hole, and the other holes in the plate are positioned from this point.

Progressive Dimensioning

The above diagrams also indicate a method known as progressive dimensioning, a device that avoids the accummulation of tolerance that may occur where "chain dimensioning" is used. Thus, all three pairs of 9 mm. diameter holes in Fig. 1·77 are marked off from the common centre-point A with the result that, for the stated general tolerance, the maximum variation in the centre distances between any pair of holes will not exceed $\pm 0·1$ mm. The comparison of this diagram with Fig. 1·78 which illustrates the use of chain dimensioning will clarify the above statement.

Ordinate Dimensions

In general the position of all features of shape is defined by rectangular co-ordinates, and this method is even used where a shape is curved or where holes are spaced irregularly on a common pitch circle, as shown in Fig. 1·79. An alternative method that is widely used where a profile curvature varies involves the use of polar co-ordinates, i.e. the definition of position by stating the angular displacement from a datum line and the radial distance from a datum point. An example of polar co-ordinates is shown in Fig. 1·80.

It should be noted that the choice between rectangular and polar co-ordinates will depend upon the type of machine tool that will be employed to carry out the machining operations.

49

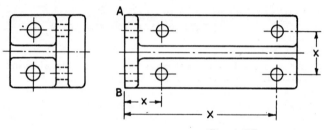

Fig. 1·75

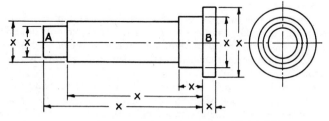

Fig. 1·76

6 HOLES 9 DIA.

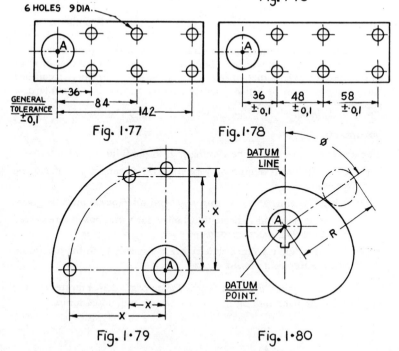

GENERAL
TOLERANCE
± 0,1

Fig. 1·77

Fig. 1·78

Fig. 1·79

Fig. 1·80

50

DIMENSIONAL CONTROL 3

Implied Limits

In the first paragraph on this subject it was said that every drawing should clearly state the accuracy required. As many drawing offices make no attempt to do this, the statement obviously needs to be clarified. Where there is no apparent control, it is generally found that the parts concerned are always made in the same works, where established practice and standard tools may be relied upon to give satisfactory results. This does not mean that control is unnecessary or non-existent; clearly it is left to the discretion of the makers who have earned a reputation for both the quality and accuracy of their work.

An alternative method that is widely used is a system of "Implied Limits" which generally involves the use or letters of symbols to indicate (a) the dimensions that are important and (b) the degree of accuracy that is required. Under certain conditions this method of control is entirely satisfactory.

However, with the rapid expansion of the Engineering Industry and the increasing use of mass-production methods, it has been found worth while to sub-contract a large amount of work that is of a specialized nature. In these circumstances the initial assembly and the subsequent replacement of worn parts would be either extremely difficult or quite impossible unless the control of size was rigidly exercised. This is suitably emphasized by quoting a relevant passage from B.S. 308 which says, "Tolerance should be specified for all requirements critical to functioning and interchangeability wherever it is doubtful (as, for example, in most sub-contracted work) that ordinary or established workshop technique and equipment can be relied upon to achieve a satisfactory standard of accuracy."

Summary

The above comments may be summarized in the following manner:—

(1) Very fine limits should only be imposed to satisfy manufacturing necessity.

(2) Where circumstances permit, a general tolerance should be given.

(3) Tolerances should indicate unusually wide variations in size as well as extremely small variations.

(4) An individual tolerance should directly specify both the maximum and the minimum limits of size.

The detail drawing, Fig. 1·81 on the facing page, demonstrates the use of general tolerances and, on the same drawing, individual limits.

51

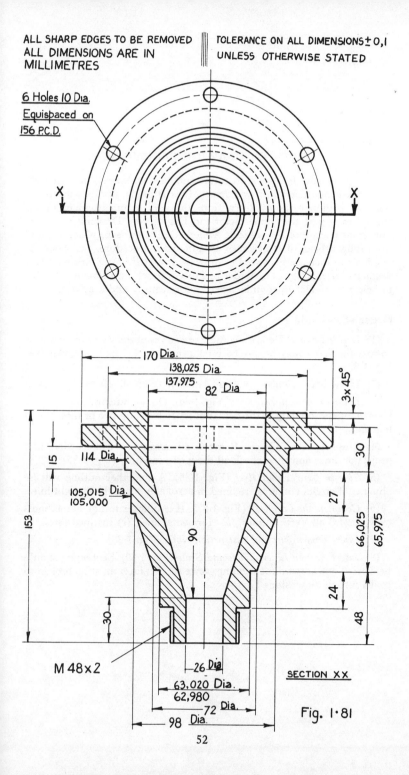

ALL SHARP EDGES TO BE REMOVED ||| TOLERANCE ON ALL DIMENSIONS ± 0,1
ALL DIMENSIONS ARE IN   UNLESS OTHERWISE STATED
MILLIMETRES

6 Holes 10 Dia.
Equispaced on
156 P.C.D.

X ——— X

170 Dia.
138,025 Dia.
137,975
82 Dia
3 x 45°

30

114 Dia.

15

105,015 Dia.
105,000

153

90

27

66,025
65,975

24

48

30

M 48 x 2

26 Dia.

63,020 Dia.
62,980

72 Dia.

98 Dia.

SECTION XX

Fig. 1·81

52

ORDER OF DRAWING PROCEDURE

Examination and industrial requirements demand neat and accurate drawings *within stipulated time limits*. It is strongly advised, therefore, that the beginner should learn from the very commencement of his studies to regard the "time factor" in Engineering Drawing as a very important feature of the subject. A methodical approach, which if practised diligently until it becomes an automatic procedure, will help the beginner to increase his speed of drawing and *at the same time retain his neatness and accuracy*. The Order of Procedure set out below is intended to help the student to combine speed with neatness and accuracy.

Order of Procedure

(1) *Decide Layout.* Determine the *overall* sizes of the views to be drawn so that the views may be spaced intelligently on the drawing paper (see Fig. 1·82).

(2) Insert Main Centre Lines or datum lines on all Views (Fig. 1·83).

(3) *Draw in the required views* (Fig. 1·84). Do not attempt to finish one view before proceeding to the next, but try to build up two or three views together.

(4) *Clean up and Check.* Remove all unwanted construction and projection lines and then check all the views carefully (Fig. 1·85).

(5) *Line-in Circles and Arcs* (Fig. 1·86). A smoother outline will be obtained if circles and arcs are lined in BEFORE lining in the straight lines.

(6) *Complete the Lining In* (Fig. 1·87). It is quicker to line in methodically, i.e. (a) all Vertical lines, (b) Horizontal lines, (c) Inclined lines.

(7) *Insert Dimensions and Instruction Notes* (Fig. 1·88).

(8) *Insert Section Lines, Titles and Scale* (Fig. 1·89). Sectioning should be carried out AFTER dimensioning, since section lines must be broken to avoid cutting dimensions.

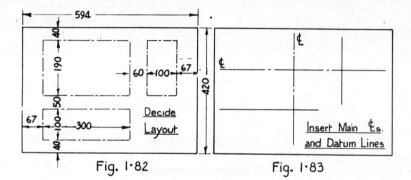

Fig. 1·82

Fig. 1·83

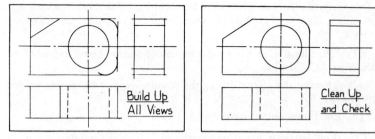

Fig. 1·84

Fig. 1·85

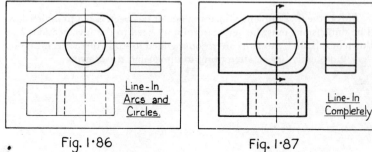

Fig. 1·86

Fig. 1·87

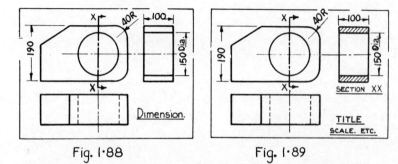

Fig. 1·88

Fig. 1·89

E

54

SECTIONAL VIEWS

Problem Assignments

Exercise 1

Two views of a Terminal Block are shown at Fig. 1·90. Draw to a scale 4/1, in either First or Third Angle Orthographic Projection, the following views:

(1) A Sectional End View—the planes of section being indicated by the lines AC, DE, FG.

(2) A Sectional Inverted Plan—the plane of section being represented by the line BB.

(3) The Elevation as given.

Insert hidden detail where necessary and fully dimension the completed drawing.

NOTES

This is the first drawing which the reader has been asked to dimension. The dimensions must be very carefully inserted to the specifications laid down in B.S. 308. Students are recommended to study these specifications very thoroughly before attempting to dimension the drawing.

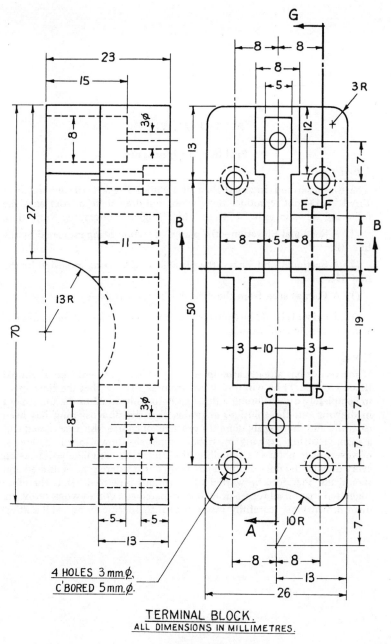

4 HOLES 3 mm.∅,
C'BORED 5 mm.∅.

TERMINAL BLOCK.
ALL DIMENSIONS IN MILLIMETRES.

Fig. 1·90

56

SECTIONAL VIEWS

Problem Assignments

Exercise 2

The Elevation and Inverted Plan of a Pulley Bracket are illustrated at Fig. 1·91. Do not reproduce these views, but draw instead, FULL SIZE, the following views in either First or Third Angle Orthographic Projection:

(1) A Sectional Elevation—the planes of section being indicated by the line BB.

(2) A Sectional End View—the plane of section being indicated by the line XX.

(3) A Plan as seen from the direction of the Arrow A.

Hidden detail should be shown where necessary. Insert SIX main dimensions on the finished drawing.

NOTES

If the reader has already attempted the previous problem (the Terminal Block Exercise 1) he will now know from experience that the time spent in completely dimensioning a drawing is roughly equal to the time spent in drawing out the solution, assuming that the dimensioning has been carefully and thoroughly done. In practice, of course, this is accepted and a manufacturing drawing must be completely dimensioned. There is, however, little point in compelling the student to completely dimension every drawing he does during a drawing course where time is limited and should not therefore be wasted upon tedious repetition. It is therefore suggested that on all future drawings prepared FOR COURSEWORK ONLY six main dimensions—carefully inserted to B.S. specifications—will suffice.

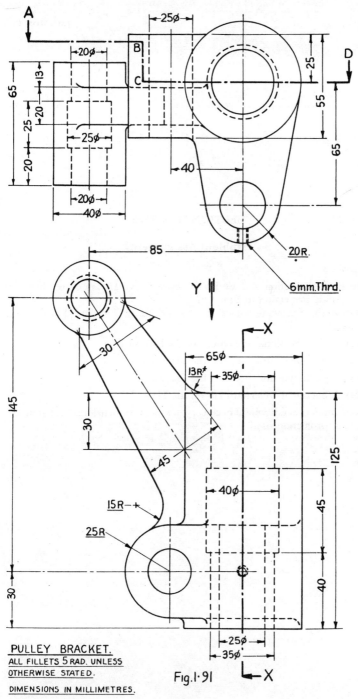

PULLEY BRACKET.
ALL FILLETS 5 RAD. UNLESS
OTHERWISE STATED.

DIMENSIONS IN MILLIMETRES.

Fig.1·91

58

SECTIONAL VIEWS

Problem Assignments

Exercise 3

The Front Elevation and End View of a Sleeve Housing are shown in First Angle Projection in Fig. 1·92.

Draw the following views FULL SIZE and in First or Third Angle Projection:

(1) A Half Sectional Elevation on the Plane BB.

(2) A Sectional End View on the Plane CC.

(3) A Sectional End View on the Plane DD.

(4) A Sectional Inverted Plan on the Plane AA.

Insert hidden detail where necessary, six main dimensions, and state the angle of projection used.

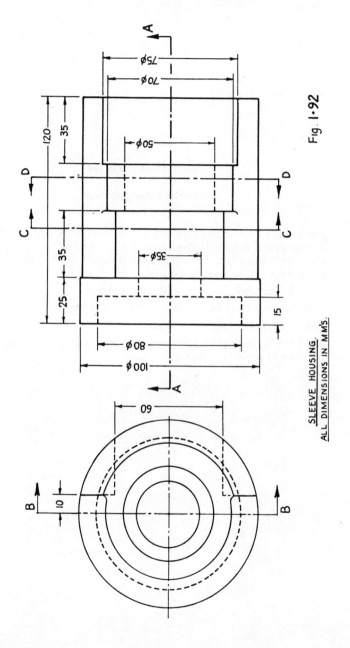

Fig. 1·92

SLEEVE HOUSING.
ALL DIMENSIONS IN MMS.

SECTIONAL VIEWS

Problem Assignments

Exercise 4

The Front Elevation and Plan of a Cover Bracket for a Mixing Machine are shown in First Angle Projection in Fig. 1·93.

Do not copy these views but draw FULL SIZE and in either First or Third Angle Projection the following:

(1) A Sectional Elevation on the Plane AA.

(2) An End View looking in the direction of the Arrow B.

(3) A Sectional Plan on the Plane CC.

Insert the hidden detail where necessary, six main dimensions, and state the angle of projection used.

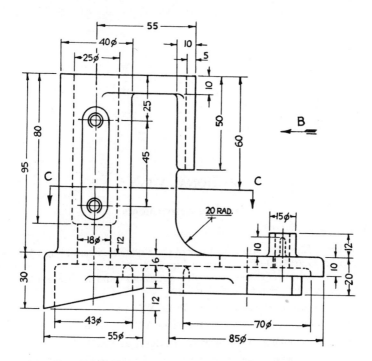

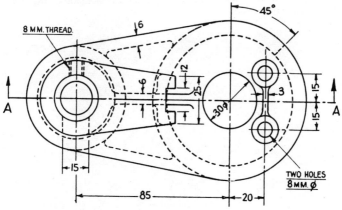

COVER BRACKET FOR MIXER.
ALL FILLETS ARE 3 MM. RADIUS.
ALL DIMENSIONS ARE IN MM'S.

Fig. 1·93

SECTIONAL VIEWS

Problem Assignments

Exercise 5

The Front Elevation and End View of the Body of a Scaffolding Clip are shown in First Angle Projection in Fig. 1·94.

Do not copy these views but draw FULL SIZE and in either First or Third Angle Projection the following:

(1) A Sectional Elevation on the Plane XX.

(2) A Sectional End View on the Plane YY.

(3) A Plan looking in the direction of the Arrow Z.

Insert hidden detail where necessary, six main dimensions, and state the angle of projection used.

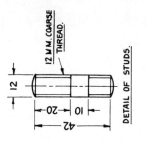

12 M.M. COARSE THREAD.

12

42
20
10

DETAIL OF STUDS.

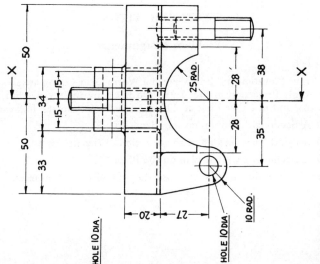

50
50
X
34
15
15
50
33
25 RAD.
28
28
38
35
X
20
27

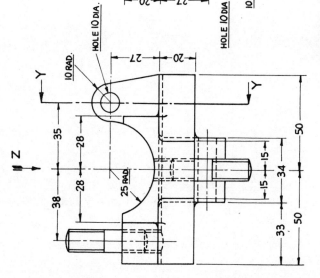

10 RAD.
HOLE 10 DIA.
Y
35
28
28
38
33
27
20
25 RAD.
Z
15
34
15
50
50
Y

HOLE 10 DIA.
10 RAD.

SCAFFOLDING CLIP BODY.
ALL FILLETS ARE 3MM'S RADIUS.
ALL DIMENSIONS ARE IN M M'S.

Fig: 1·94.

64

SECTIONAL VIEWS

Problem Assignments

Exercise 6

The Front Elevation and End View of a Worm Gear Casing are shown in First Angle Projection in Fig. 1·95. Do not copy these views but draw FULL SIZE and in either First or Third Angle Projection the following:

(1) A Sectional Elevation on the Plane AA.

(2) An End View looking in the direction of the Arrow B.

(3) A Sectional Inverted Plan on the Plane CC.

Insert six main dimensions and state the type of projection used.

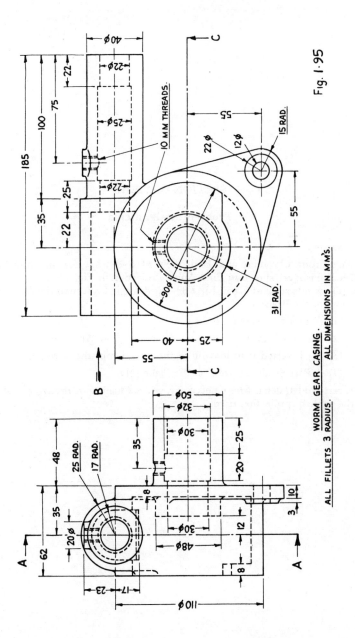

WORM GEAR CASING.

ALL DIMENSIONS IN MMS.

ALL FILLETS 3 RADIUS.

Fig. 1.95

66

SECTIONAL VIEWS

Problem Assignments

Exercise 7

The Front Elevation and End View of a Bracket for an Auto-feed Mechanism are shown in First Angle Projection in Fig. 1·96.

Draw to a scale of 2/1 in First or Third Angle Projection the following views of the Bracket:

(1) A Front Elevation as View A.

(2) An End View looking in the direction of the Arrow B.

(3) An Inverted Plan looking in the direction of the Arrow C.

(4) A Part Sectional View on the Plane DD.

Insert hidden detail where necessary, add six main dimensions, and state the angle of projection used.

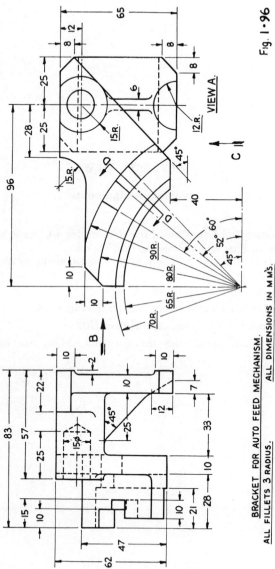

VIEW A.

BRACKET FOR AUTO FEED MECHANISM.
ALL DIMENSIONS IN MMS.
ALL FILLETS 3 RADIUS.

Fig. 1·96

68

SECTIONAL VIEWS

Problem Assignments

Exercise 8 ·

The Elevation and End View of the Housing for a Control Mechanism are shown in First Angle Projection in Fig. 1·97.

Draw FULL SIZE and in Third Angle Projection the following views of the Housing:

(1) The Given Elevation, View A.

(2) A Half Sectional Inverted Plan on the Plane AA.

(3) A Sectional End View on the Plane BB.

Insert the hidden detail where necessary and add six main dimensions.

69

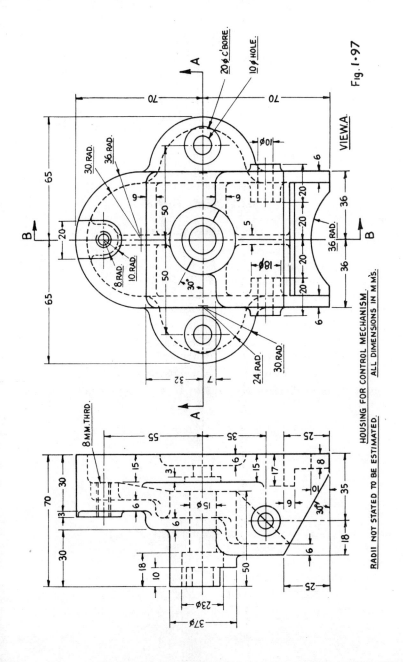

20 φ C'BORE.

10 φ HOLE.

Fig. 1·97

VIEW A.

HOUSING FOR CONTROL MECHANISM.
ALL DIMENSIONS IN M.M⁵.

RADII NOT STATED TO BE ESTIMATED.

F

70

SECTIONAL VIEWS

Problem Assignments

Exercise 9

The Front Elevation, End View and Plan of a Nozzle for a Vacuum Cleaner are shown in First Angle Projection in Fig. 1·98.

Do not copy the views but draw FULL SIZE and in First Angle Projection the following:

(1) A Half Sectional Elevation on the Plane AA.

(2) A Sectional End View on the Plane BB—this view to be projected to the right of the Half Sectional Elevation AA.

(3) An Inverted Plan looking in the direction of Arrow C.

Insert six main dimensions. Hidden Detail may be omitted from all views.

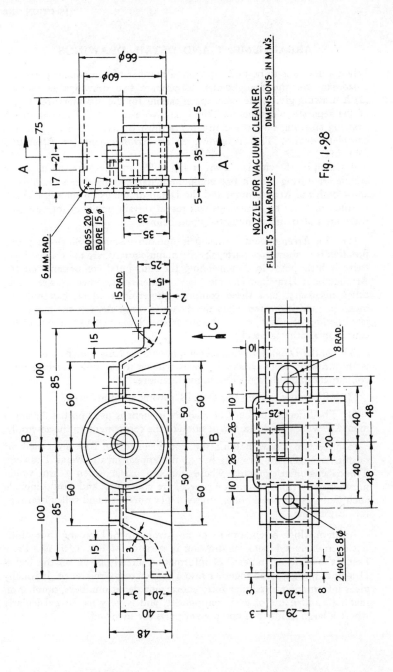

NOZZLE FOR VACUUM CLEANER.
FILLETS 3 M.M. RADIUS.
DIMENSIONS IN M M'S.

Fig. 1·98

ϕ99
ϕ60
75
21
17
35
5
5
33
35
BOSS 20 ϕ
BORE 15 ϕ
6 M.M. RAD.
A
A

15 RAD.
25
15
2
15
100
85
60
50
60
B
B
60
50
60
100
85
15
3
20
3
40
48
C

8 RAD.
10
10
26
26
25
20
40
48
40
48
10
2 HOLES 8 ϕ
3
20
3
29
8

72

ARRANGEMENT AND DETAIL DRAWINGS

When a device is to be built up from a number of component parts it is customary for the draughtsman to prepare two drawings as follows: (*a*) A drawing giving the exact specifications for the manufacture of each of the separate components. This is known as a Detail Drawing. (*b*) A drawing showing how the components must be assembled to form the complete device. This is known as an Arrangement (or Assembly) Drawing.

A Clamping Device is shown at Fig. 1·99, and because the design is simple, requiring only a few component parts, it has been possible to show both the Arrangement and the Detail drawings on the same sheet. A study of these two drawings will reveal certain points of interest, and these are noted and commented upon below.

(1) The Arrangement Drawing is not dimensioned. Since its prime function is to show how parts, already manufactured, are to be assembled, there is little point in dimensioning the individual components on the Arrangement Drawing. Certain "key" dimensions, however, are sometimes necessary, and these comprise dimensions which can only be measured and inspected when the device is complete, e.g. the maximum jaw opening of a vice, or the height from a lathe bed to the axis of the centre on a lathe tailstock.

(2) On the Detail Drawing all components are fully dimensioned. This is the drawing from which the parts will be made and therefore must contain complete data relative to manufacture.

(3) All components on the Detail Drawing are numbered.

(4) The "detail number" of each component is used on the Arrangement Drawing to indicate the position of the component on the assembly.

(5) The two screws holding the End Plate to the Base are called for on the Arrangement Drawing but do not appear on the Detail Drawing. This is customary practice where standard parts, which a firm would normally buy from an outside source, are concerned and would include such items as standard bolts, screws, taper pins, ball and roller bearings, lubricators, etc.

An item which often appears on an Arrangement Drawing (but which has been excluded from the drawing illustration at Fig. 1·99) is a Parts List. It is really a "repeat" of information already given on the Detail Drawing, but gathered together into a list for ready reference. It usually gives information in tabular form concerning detail numbers, number of, material, and name of each component, and is very useful particularly where a large number of component parts are involved.

73

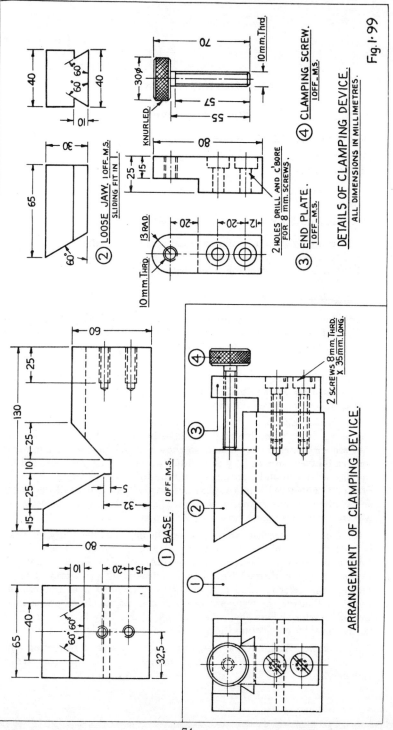

① BASE. 1 OFF - M.S.

② LOOSE JAW. 1 OFF - M.S.
SLIDING FIT IN ①

③ END PLATE. 1 OFF - M.S.

2 HOLES DRILL AND C'BORE FOR 8 mm SCREWS.

10 mm THRD.

13 RAD.

KNURLED

10 mm Thrd.

④ CLAMPING SCREW. 1 OFF - M.S.

DETAILS OF CLAMPING DEVICE.
ALL DIMENSIONS IN MILLIMETRES.

Fig. 1·99

ARRANGEMENT OF CLAMPING DEVICE.

2 SCREWS 8 mm THRD. × 35 mm LONG.

74

ARRANGEMENT DRAWINGS

Problem Assignments

Disc-Type Flexible Coupling (Fig. 1·100)

Draw, FULL SIZE, the following orthographic views of the Coupling with all parts assembled:

(1) A Sectional Elevation corresponding to the given sectional view of Detail 1.

(2) An End View in projection with (1).

The coupling should be shown keyed to the two shafts.
Approximately 100 mm length of each shaft should be drawn.
First or Third Angle Projection may be used.

BACKGROUND NOTES

A coupling is a device for connecting two shafts, whose ends abutt, in order that one shaft be driven by the other. Couplings may be divided into four main groups as follows: (a) Rigid, (b) Flexible, (c) Universal, (d) Clutches.

(a) *Rigid Couplings*, as their name implies, connect the shafts rigidly, i.e. no backlash is permitted. In addition, the two shafts must be in exact alignment otherwise serious stresses will be induced.

(b) *Flexible Couplings* allow a slight misalignment between the shafts and also provide a "cushioning" effect when sudden changes of speed or load are encountered. In the pattern chosen for the problem assignment, the flexibility is provided by the leather washers which are mounted on the disc as shown and transmit the torque from the driving shaft to the driven. The flanges of the coupling are pressed on the ends of the shafts and further secured by means of feather keys. This coupling as designed will transmit 96 h.p. at a speed of 1200 r.p.m.

(c) *Universal Couplings* are used when the degree of flexibility required is greater than could be provided by a flexible coupling. The Hooke's Joint is probably the best known type and will allow shafts inclined at angles of not more than 30 degrees to be satisfactorily connected. Unfortunately the velocity ratio of two shafts so inclined does not remain constant. This may be overcome by mounting *two* couplings, one at each end of an intermediate shaft. An example of this may be seen on a car where the shaft connecting the gear-box to the rear axle is so treated.

(d) *Clutches*. A clutch is a coupling which is designed to permit slip between the driver and driven shafts whenever the load or speed varies suddenly.

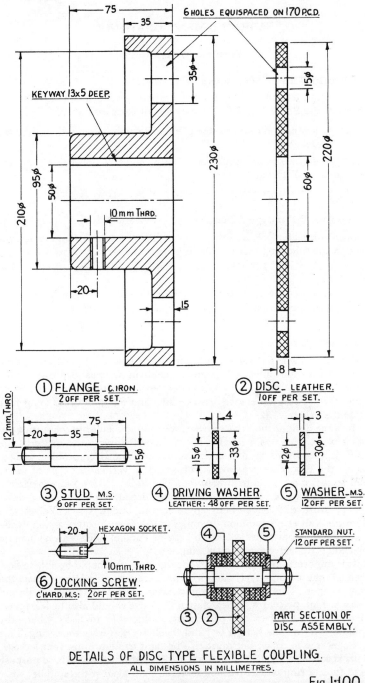

75

35

6 HOLES EQUISPACED ON 170 P.C.D.

KEYWAY 13×5 DEEP.

35⌀

15⌀

230⌀

220⌀

210⌀

95⌀

50⌀

60⌀

10 mm THRD.

20

15

8

① FLANGE – C.IRON.
2 OFF PER SET.

② DISC – LEATHER.
1 OFF PER SET.

12 mm THRD.

75

20 35

15⌀

4

15⌀ 33⌀

3

12⌀ 30⌀

③ STUD – M.S.
6 OFF PER SET.

④ DRIVING WASHER.
LEATHER: 48 OFF PER SET.

⑤ WASHER – M.S.
12 OFF PER SET.

20

HEXAGON SOCKET.

10 mm THRD.

⑥ LOCKING SCREW.
C'HARD. M.S: 2 OFF PER SET.

④ ⑤

STANDARD NUT.
12 OFF PER SET.

③ ②

PART SECTION OF
DISC ASSEMBLY.

DETAILS OF DISC TYPE FLEXIBLE COUPLING.
ALL DIMENSIONS IN MILLIMETRES.

76

Fig. 1·100

ARRANGEMENT DRAWINGS

Problem Assignments

1. 45 mm Boiler Check Valve (Fig. 1-101)

Draw, FULL SIZE and in either First or Third Angle Projection the following views of the Boiler Check Valve showing all parts assembled:

(1) A Sectional Elevation—the plane of section being indicated by the line XX Detail 4.

(2) A Half Sectional End View—the plane of section being indicated by the line YY Detail 4.

(3) A Plan as seen from the direction of the Arrow A Detail 4.

2. 20 mm Pillar-type Bibcock (Figs. 1·102 and 1·103)

Draw, to a scale $1\frac{1}{2}/1$, in either First or Third Angle Orthographic Projection the following views of the Bibcock with all parts assembled:

(1) A Sectional Elevation corresponding to the Part Section AA Detail 1.

(2) An End View as seen from the direction of the Arrow C Detail 1.

(3) A Plan corresponding to the plan shown at Detail 1.

BACKGROUND NOTES

Valves are devices designed to control the flow of liquids and gases. There are a wide variety of designs available in practice. Some are hand-operated, others are automatic and rely either on mechanical means or upon the pressure difference between inlet and outlet in order to open or close the valve.

In some designs the valve movement is perpendicular to the seating; in other types the valve is given a sliding action; in yet other patterns the valve is hinged and has a rotary movement. In the given problem assignments the Bibcock represents hand-operated, vertical-lift type of valve, and is in fact a typical bathroom tap. The Boiler Check Valve is again a vertical-lift type of valve, but is automatic, depending for its action upon the pressure differences between inlet and outlet. Clack Valves and Throttle Valves are common examples of valves with rotary action, while Gate Valves (sometimes called Fullway or Parallel Slide Valves) operate by sliding the valve across its seating.

It is important that on all valves the liquid or gas should be able to flow through the casing freely and without excessive turbulence when the valve is open. This is particularly important when dealing with fluids and gases at high pressures. When closed, the valve should also be leakproof. Hand-operated valves are particularly vulnerable to leaks where the spindle carrying the handle or handwheel emerges from the casing. This must be free to rotate but must also be tight enough to prevent leakage. This is achieved by using a packing gland or stuffing box, whose purpose is to force a ring of soft packing material tight against the spindle.

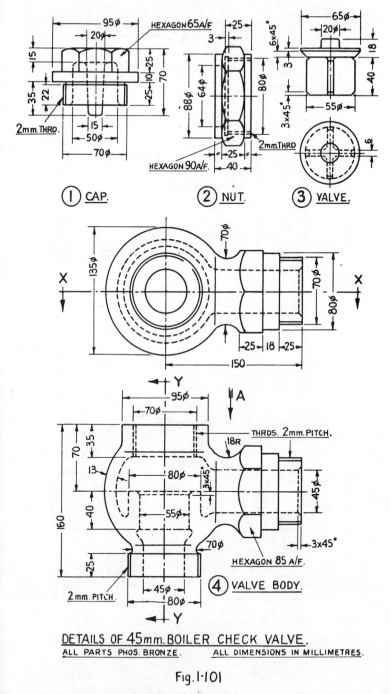

① CAP.　　② NUT.　　③ VALVE.

HEXAGON 65 A/F

2mm.THRD.

25 — 3 — HEXAGON 90 A/F.

6×45°　HEXAGON 85 A/F.

THRDS. 2mm. PITCH.

④ VALVE BODY.

2mm. PITCH.

DETAILS OF 45mm. BOILER CHECK VALVE.

ALL PARTS PHOS. BRONZE.　　ALL DIMENSIONS IN MILLIMETRES.

Fig.1·101

78

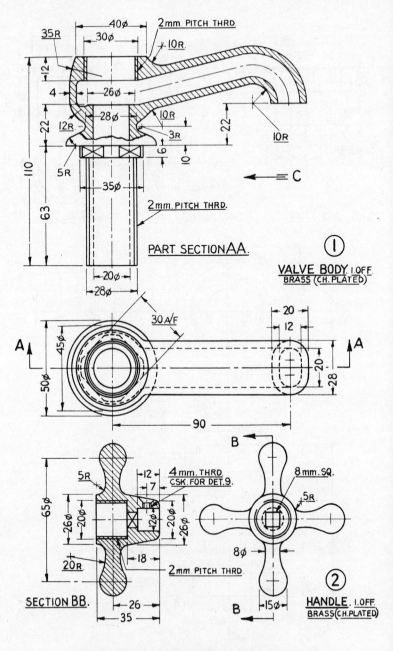

35R

40∅
30∅
2mm. PITCH THRD.

10R.

12

4   26∅

28∅   10R

3R

12R   6

10

5R   2mm.PITCH THRD.

35∅

110   63

20∅
28∅

PART SECTION AA.

22   22

10R

◀══ C

① VALVE BODY. 1.OFF.
BRASS (CH.PLATED)

30 A/F

20
12

45∅
50∅   20
28

A ↑   ↑ A

90

B ◀

5R   4 mm. THRD.
CSK. FOR DET. 9.
12
7

8 mm. SQ.

65∅   26∅   20∅
12∅   20∅   26∅

5R

20R   18

8∅

SECTION BB.   2mm PITCH THRD.

26
35

15∅

② HANDLE. 1.OFF.
BRASS(CH.PLATED)

B ◀

DETAILS OF PILLAR TYPE 20MM. BIBCOCK.
ALL DIMENSIONS IN MILLIMETRES.

Fig.1·102

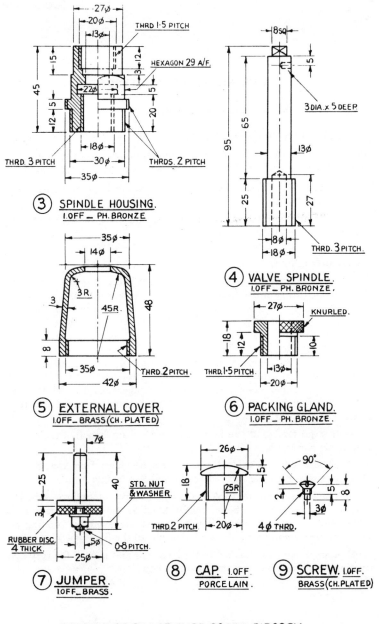

③ SPINDLE HOUSING.
1 OFF — PH. BRONZE

④ VALVE SPINDLE.
1 OFF — PH. BRONZE.

⑤ EXTERNAL COVER.
1 OFF — BRASS (CH. PLATED)

⑥ PACKING GLAND.
1 OFF — PH. BRONZE.

⑦ JUMPER.
1 OFF — BRASS.

⑧ CAP. 1 OFF.
PORCELAIN.

⑨ SCREW. 1 OFF.
BRASS (CH. PLATED)

DETAILS OF PILLAR TYPE 20 MM. BIBCOCK.
ALL DIMENSIONS IN MILLIMETRES.

Fig. 1·103

SHEET 2 OF 2.

ARRANGEMENT DRAWINGS

Problem Assignments

3. **Small Bench Vice** (Figs. 1·104 and 1·105)

Draw, to a scale 1½/1, the following orthographic views of the Bench Vice with all parts assembled. First or Third Angle projection may be used:

(1) A Sectional Elevation corresponding to the Section YY shown at Detail 1 Sheet 1.

(2) An End View corresponding to the end view shown at Detail 1 Sheet 1.

BACKGROUND NOTES

A vice is a holding fixture—its prime function being to grip a component firmly while fitting or machining operations are carried out. The majority of vices consist of two jaws, one of which is fixed and the other movable. (An exception is the Pin Vice, in which both jaws are adjustable.) The fixed jaw is usually cast solid with the vice body while the movable jaw travels in a guide cut into the vice body and is actuated by means of a screw. The small Bench Vice set for the problem assignment is of a pattern used frequently by Watchmakers and Instrument makers for holding very small components. When compared with the standard Engineers' Bench Vice, certain differences become apparent and these features are set out below.

(1) It is portable and can be readily fixed to any bench or table top of reasonable thickness.

(2) The loose (or movable) jaw is that furthest away from the operator. (The reverse is the case with an Engineers' Bench Vice.)

(3) The travel of the movable jaw is achieved by rotating the actuating nut, the actuating screw being rigidly fixed to the movable jaw. (The movement on an Engineers' Bench Vice is achieved by rotating the actuating screw and fixing the actuating nut to the fixed jaw.)

(4) A small anvil is attached to the loose jaw and is used for very light riveting operations on very small components.

ARRANGEMENT DRAWINGS

Problem Assignments

4. 125 mm Self-Aligning Roller-Bearing Plummer Block (Figs. 1·106 and 1·107)

Draw, to a scale half FULL SIZE, the following orthographic views of the Plummer Block with all the parts assembled. First or Third Angle Projection may be used:

(1) A Half Sectional Elevation corresponding to the Half Section AA shown at Detail 1 Sheet 1.

(2) A Half Sectional End View—the plane of section to contain the axis of the shaft.

(3) Project a Plan showing the left-hand half with the Top Cap removed.

Insert a suitable lubricating device in the Top Cap.

BACKGROUND NOTES

A bearing is a device designed to support a rotating shaft. Its essential features are (*a*) minimum frictional resistance to rotation, (*b*) adequate provision for lubrication. A wide variety of types are in general use, and when selecting a suitable bearing for a particular application a number of factors must be considered including:

(1) Type of load—e.g. Thrust or Journal (Thrust is the load parallel to the axis of the shaft).

(2) Magnitude of load.

(3) Speed of Shaft.

(4) Accessibility of bearing for purposes of maintenance and lubrication.

(5) Cost, etc.

In modern practice ball and roller bearings are extensively used because although the initial cost is high they will take considerable loads, will run satisfactorily over a wide range of speeds and require little maintenance during their useful life, which is generally much longer than that of most other types of bearing.

The Self-Aligning Roller Bearing Plummer Block which has been selected for the problem assignment is suitable for heavy journal loads and would transmit a load of 10 000 kg at a speed of approximately 500 r.p.m.

The partly spherical seating for the outer race permits the roller bearing to adjust its position to compensate for any slight misalignment of the shaft relative to the block. The function of the felt pads is to exclude dirt and to retain lubricant.

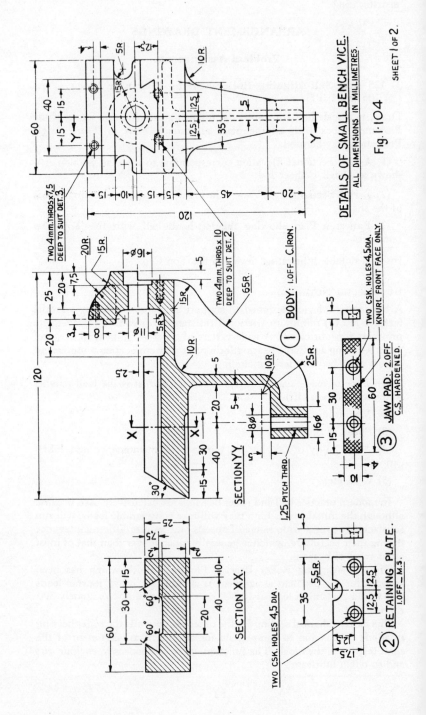

DETAILS OF SMALL BENCH VICE.
ALL DIMENSIONS IN MILLIMETRES.

Fig. 1·104

SHEET 1 OF 2.

① BODY: 1 OFF. C. IRON.

② RETAINING PLATE. 1 OFF. M.S.

③ JAW PAD: 2 OFF. C.S. HARDENED.

SECTION YY.

SECTION XX.

83

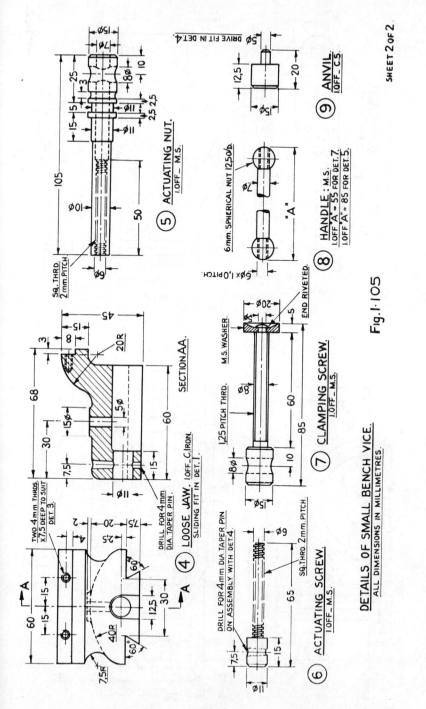

DETAILS OF SMALL BENCH VICE.
ALL DIMENSIONS IN MILLIMETRES.

Fig. 1·105

④ **LOOSE JAW.** 1 OFF—C.IRON.
SECTION AA.

⑤ **ACTUATING NUT.** 1 OFF—M.S.
SQ. THRD. 2 mm. PITCH

⑥ **ACTUATING SCREW.** 1 OFF—M.S.
SQ. THRD. 2 mm. PITCH.
DRILL FOR 4mm DIA TAPER PIN ON ASSEMBLY WITH DET. 4.

⑦ **CLAMPING SCREW.** 1 OFF—M.S.
1·25 PITCH THRD.
M.S. WASHER.
END RIVETED.

⑧ **HANDLE : M.S.**
1 OFF "A" = 55 FOR DET. 7
1 OFF "A" = 85 FOR DET. 5.
6mm. SPHERICAL NUT 12·5 DIA.

⑨ **ANVIL.** 1 OFF—C.S.
DRIVE FIT IN DET. 4.

84

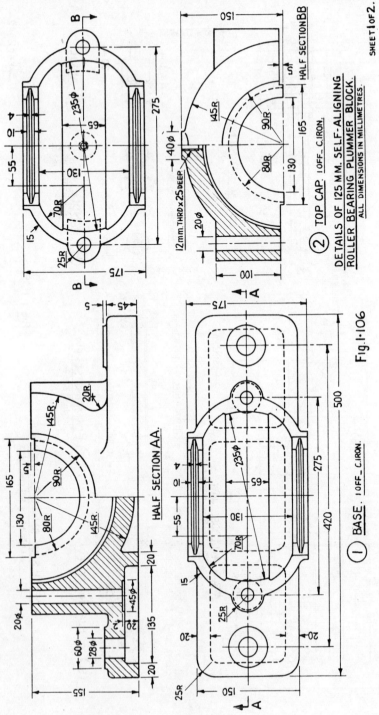

HALF SECTION AA.

① BASE. 1 OFF. C.IRON.

Fig.1·106

② TOP CAP. 1 OFF. C.IRON.
HALF SECTION BB

12mm.THRD x 25 DEEP

DETAILS OF 125 MM. SELF-ALIGNING
ROLLER BEARING PLUMMER BLOCK.
ALL DIMENSIONS IN MILLIMETRES.

85

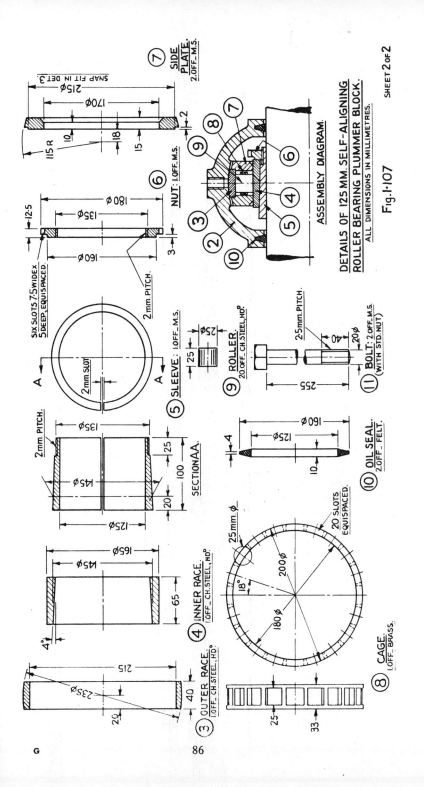

SIDE PLATE. 2.OFF. M.S. (7)

SNAP FIT IN DET 3.
215⌀
170⌀
115 R
10
18
15
2

NUT: 1.OFF. M.S. (6)

12·5
180⌀
135⌀
160⌀
3
2mm.PITCH.

SIX SLOTS 7.5 WIDE ×
5 DEEP, EQUISPACED.

2mm SLOT
A
A

SLEEVE: 1.OFF. M.S. (5)
25⌀
25

ROLLER. (9)
20 OFF. CH.STEEL, HD°.

BOLT: 2.OFF. M.S. (11)
(WITH STD. NUT)
25mm.PITCH.
40
20⌀
255

SECTION A.A.
2mm.PITCH.
135⌀
145⌀
125⌀
25
100
20

OIL SEAL. (10)
2.OFF. FELT.
160⌀
125⌀
4
10

INNER RACE. (4)
1.OFF - CH.STEEL, HD°.
165⌀
145⌀
65
4°

OUTER RACE. (3)
1.OFF - CH.STEEL, HD°.
215
235⌀
40
20

CAGE. (8)
1.OFF - BRASS.
25mm ⌀
200 ⌀
18°
180 ⌀
20 SLOTS
EQUISPACED.
25
33

ASSEMBLY DIAGRAM.
7
8
9
6
3
2
4
10
5

DETAILS OF 125 MM. SELF-ALIGNING
ROLLER BEARING PLUMMER BLOCK.
ALL DIMENSIONS IN MILLIMETRES.

Fig.1·107

SHEET 2 OF 2

G   86

MULTI-START SCREW THREADS

Although it has been stated in the preface that certain items, including screw threads, will not be dealt with in detail in this book, the authors feel that a brief discussion on Single and Multi-Start screw threads should be included at this stage, before the student attempts the solution of the next problem—the Flypress (Figs. 1·108 and 1·109).

If a point moves round the curved surface of a cylinder and simultaneously advances along the cylinder in a direction parallel to its axis (the ratio of the two velocities being constant) the path traced by the moving point will be a HELIX. The axial distance travelled by the point during 360 degrees of its rotary motion is called the PITCH.

A screw thread is a helical groove.

If a screw thread is formed by means of ONE helical groove it is known as a SINGLE START thread, and one complete revolution of the nut, relative to the screw, will cause the nut to advance along the screw a distance equal to the pitch of the thread.

When screw threads are used for the transmission of power it is often desirable that the axial travel of the nut relative to the screw should be considerably more than one pitch of the thread per revolution. Increased travel per revolution may be achieved by the use of MULTI-START threads. If a screw thread is formed by means of TWO or MORE identical helical grooves it is known as a MULTI-START thread. Consider initially a single start square thread having a 6 mm pitch. The depth and width of the groove would thus be 3 mm and the nut would advance 6 mm per revolution. Next, consider a square thread having a 12 mm pitch *but with the same groove dimensions* 3 mm × 3 mm *as above.* Careful thought will show that there is now space to cut a second idential thread on the same cylinder provided the second thread is started exactly 180 degrees round the cylinder from the start of the first thread. This is a 2 START thread. It has a 6 mm pitch but the nut would now advance 12 mm per revolution.

When dealing with multi-start threads, the distance travelled by the nut per revolution is called the LEAD.

LEAD = PITCH × Number of STARTS

When drawing multi-start threads conventionally (see Detail 7, Fig. 1·109), the slope of the threads is obtained by advancing one side relative to the other by an amount equal to $\frac{\text{LEAD}}{2}$.

87

ARRANGEMENT DRAWINGS

Problem Assignments

7. Flypress (Figs. 1·108 and 1·109)

Draw, to a scale of HALF FULL SIZE (using A1 Size drawing paper), the following views of the Flypress with all parts assembled. First or Third Angle Orthographic Projection may be used:

(1) A Sectional Elevation—the plane of section being indicated by the line XX (Detail 1).

(2) An End View corresponding to the given end view on Detail 1.

(3) A Plan.

BACKGROUND NOTES

The Flypress is a hand-operated press. Any pressing operation that can be carried out on a power-operated press can also be performed on a Flypress but on a much smaller scale. The press depends for its power upon the kinetic energy stored in a fly-weight mounted upon an arm one end of which is bent upwards to receive the weight. The arm is fixed to a spindle on which is cut a multi-start, coarse-pitch screw thread. The thread converts the rotary motion of the arm and flyweight into vertical (or axial) movement. The tool holder is attached to the other end of the screwed spindle and is constrained to move along vertical guides cut into the main body of the press. The other end of the arm is bent downwards to form a handle for the use of the operator. In some of the larger flypresses the arm is bent upwards at *both* ends in order that *two* flyweights may be mounted, thus improving the balance of the press and increasing the force of the blow.

The flypress is one of the few machines whose design has remained virtually unaltered since it was first introduced, but in the modern workshop there are still many jobs for which it is ideally suited. It is often uneconomical to use a power press for an odd job such as pressing a liner or bush into a drill jig—or stamping serial numbers on a small batch of components. It is on jobs such as these that the flypress is generally used.

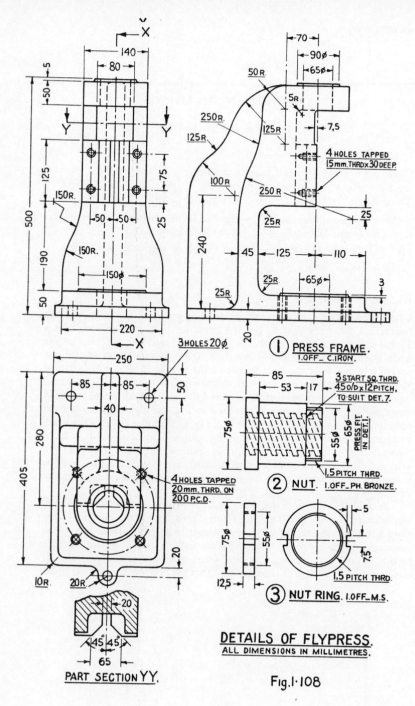

① PRESS FRAME.
1.OFF - C.IRON.

② NUT. 1.OFF - PH. BRONZE.

③ NUT RING. 1.OFF - M.S.

PART SECTION YY.

DETAILS OF FLYPRESS.
ALL DIMENSIONS IN MILLIMETRES.

Fig.1·108

89

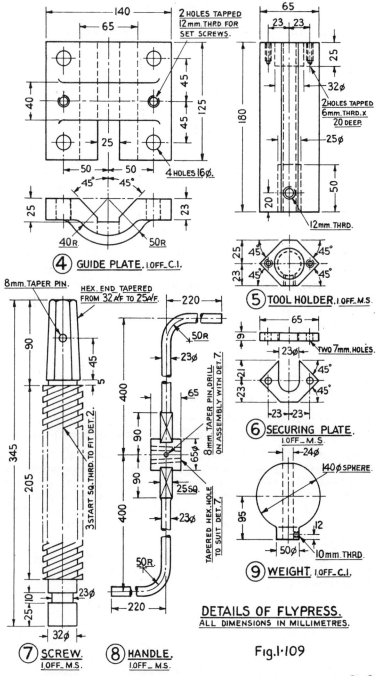

140

65

2 HOLES TAPPED 12mm. THRD. FOR SET SCREWS.

65

23 23

25

32∅

2 HOLES TAPPED 6mm. THRD. X 20 DEEP.

40

45

125

45

25∅

180

50

25

50

50

4 HOLES 16∅.

12mm. THRD.

25

45°   45°

23

25

45°   45°

45°   45°

40R   50R

④ GUIDE PLATE. 1.OFF. C.I.

⑤ TOOL HOLDER. 1.OFF. M.S.

8mm. TAPER PIN.

HEX. END TAPERED FROM 32 A/F TO 25 A/F.

220

50R

23∅

65

TWO 7mm. HOLES.

9

23∅

23

21

90

45

5

400

65

45°

45°

3 START SQ. THRD. TO FIT DET. 2.

90

23   23

345

8mm. TAPER PIN, DRILL ON ASSEMBLY WITH DET. 7.

65∅

⑥ SECURING PLATE.
1.OFF. M.S.

205

90

25 SQ.

24∅

140∅ SPHERE.

TAPERED HEX. HOLE TO SUIT DET. 7.

400

23∅

95

12

50R

25 10

23∅

220

50∅   10mm. THRD.

32∅

⑨ WEIGHT. 1.OFF. C.I.

⑦ SCREW.
1.OFF. M.S.

⑧ HANDLE.
1.OFF. M.S.

DETAILS OF FLYPRESS.
ALL DIMENSIONS IN MILLIMETRES.

Fig. 1·109

SHEET 2 OF 2.

90

PICTORIAL PROJECTIONS

Introduction

Pictorial projections may be classified under three main headings: (*a*) Perspective, (*b*) Axonometric and (*c*) Oblique, and these in turn may be further subdivided into smaller groups. The title "Pictorial" projections is a general term referring to all projections which create a three-dimensional impression by indicating length, width and height on one view. An object is more easily visualized from a pictorial view than from its orthographic projections, although the latter gives more detailed and precise information.

Perspective Projection (Figs. 2·1 and 2·2)

Perspective projection presents the object *exactly* as the eye would see it. The view is projected on the picture plane by conical projectors which converge to form a point known as the Station Point. *The object is placed in front of the picture plane and at any convenient angle to it. The projected view shows how the object would appear if observed from the station point. Edges which are parallel on the object are drawn as converging lines on the perspective view, and these lines, if produced, would meet at points called Vanishing Points situated on the viewer's horizon (see Fig. 2·2). There are three types of perspective projection:

(1) Single Point Perspective (utilizes only one vanishing point).

(2) Two Point Perspective (utilizes two vanishing points).

(3) Three Point Perspective (utilizes three vanishing points).

Despite the fact that perspective projection produces the "perfect" pictorial view, Engineers generally prefer to use the more easily drawn Axonometric and Oblique projections. Perspective projection is discussed here for the sake of completeness; the reader who wishes to study the subject further is advised to refer to one of the many books prepared for Architects and Technical Illustrators, in which perspective views are dealt with in detail.

* In order that the drawing may be kept to a reasonable size the picture plane is often considered to be transparent and placed between the object and the observer.

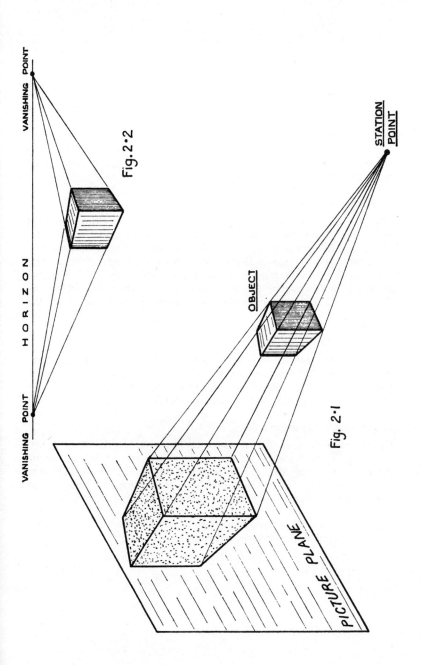

VANISHING POINT

Fig.2·2

H O R I Z O N

VANISHING POINT

STATION POINT

OBJECT

Fig. 2·1

PICTURE PLANE

92

AXONOMETRIC PROJECTION

In Axonometric projection the projector lines from the object to the picture plane are orthographic, i.e. they are perpendicular to the plane and are thus parallel to each other. There are three types of axonometric projection: (a) Dimetric, (b) Trimetric, (c) Isometric.

(a) Dimetric Projection (Fig. 2·3)

The object is set at an angle to the picture plane so that any two of its three dimensions (length and width, width and height, or length and height) are equally foreshortened on the projected view, the third dimension is foreshortened to a different degree. Thus when drawing a dimetric view of an object *two* scales must be used. In the block illustrated at Fig. 2·3, length and width may be drawn to the same scale since both are equally foreshortened, but a separate scale is necessary in order to set out the heights.

(b) Trimetric Projection (Fig. 2·4)

The object is set at such an angle to the picture plane that lengths, widths and heights are foreshortened on the projected view to a different degree. Thus when drawing trimetric views, three scales must be used—one for lengths—one for widths and a third for heights.

(c) Isometric Projection (Fig. 2·5)

The object is set at an angle to the picture plane so that its three dimensions, length, width and height, are equally foreshortened. When drawing isometric views, *only one scale* is used. For this reason the engineer uses isometric projection in preference to dimetric and trimetric although the two latter types frequently give more balanced views of the object.

In all axonometric projections edges which are parallel on the object are drawn parallel on the projected views.

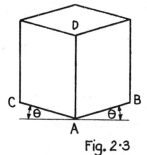

AB & AC are drawn to the same scale.

AD is drawn to a different scale.

Θ is any convenient angle.

DIMETRIC PROJECTION

Fig. 2·3

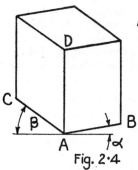

AB, AC, & AD are all drawn to different scales

β & α are different angles

TRIMETRIC PROJECTION

Fig. 2·4

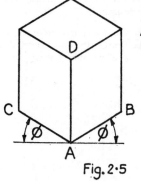

AB, AC, & AD, are all drawn to the same scale.

$\emptyset = 30°$

ISOMETRIC PROJECTION

Fig. 2·5

ISOMETRIC PROJECTION

Position of Object relative to Picture Plane

If a cube is inclined to the picture plane in such a way that *all* its faces are equally foreshortened when orthographically projected upon the plane, the projected view is the Isometric Projection of the cube. The position of the cube relative to the picture plane is best considered in two stages.

Stage 1 (see Fig. 2·6). The cube is placed with its bottom face resting on the H.P. and its horizontal edges *cb*, *cd*, etc., angled at 45 degrees to the V.P. The orthographic projections of the cube in this position are shown at Fig. 2·6. The front elevation (View A1) records an equal degree of foreshortening for *all horizontal edges*, but the vertical edges are not foreshortened at all.

Stage 2 (see Fig. 2·7). With the cube in the position described for Stage 1, rotate it about the bottom front corner C (see end view Fig. 2·7) until the body diagonal ac^1 is horizontal. In this position the front elevation of the cube (View A2) shows *all* edges equally foreshortened. View A2 is the Isometric projection of the cube. The angles $b^1 c^1 d^1$, $b^1 c^1 c$ and $d^1 c^1 c$ are each 120 degrees and can therefore be readily drawn (with the aid of a 60/30 degrees set square) directly without first drawing the orthographic views and projecting from them. This is illustrated at Fig. 2·9.* It is, however, often convenient to ignore the foreshortening altogether and to draw the isometric view to natural size. A little thought will show that in the majority of cases this will have no serious effect upon the view—it will simply make it a shade larger.

* When drawing objects which include spheres, e.g. a sphere mounted on a rectangular base, the isometric scale must be used because the dimensions of the rectangular base would be foreshortened but those of the sphere would not.

95

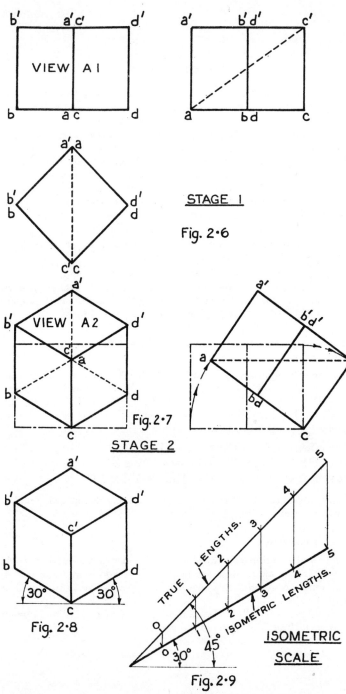

b'   a' c'   d'

VIEW A 1

b   a c   d

a'   b' d'   c'

a   b d   c

a' a

b'   d'
b   d

c' c

STAGE 1

Fig. 2·6

a'

b'   VIEW   A 2   d'

c' a

b   d

c

Fig. 2·7

STAGE 2

a'

b' d'

a   c'

b d

c

a'

b'   d'

c'

b   d

30°   c   30°

Fig. 2·8

5

4

3

TRUE LENGTHS.

2

O   1   2   3   4   5

o   ISOMETRIC LENGTHS.

30°   45°

ISOMETRIC
SCALE

Fig. 2·9

96

ISOMETRIC VIEWS

Consider the Isometric View of the cube shown at Fig. 2·10. AB, BC and BD are called the ISOMETRIC AXES and the three angles sub-tended at B are equal. Any line parallel to an Isometric Axis is known as an ISOMETRIC LINE. *Measurements may only be set off along Isometric Lines.* Lines not parallel to an Isometric Axis do not remain true to scale on an Isometric view but are distorted. Consideration of the two diagonals AD and BE will make this clear. *On the isometric view of a cube or rectangular block all edges are represented by isometric lines* and for this reason it is customary when dealing with awkward profiles to first draw the isometric view of the rectangle which would just contain the profile.

To draw an Isometric View of a Rectangular Block 50 mm × 100 mm × 75 mm high (Fig. 2·11)

Set out AB =75 mm. Draw BC =100 mm and angled at 30 degrees to the horizontal. Draw BD =50 mm and angled at 30 degrees to the horizontal. DE and FC =75 mm and are parallel to AB. AE and GF =50 mm and are parallel to BD. GE and AF =100 mm and are parallel to BC.

To draw an Isometric View of a Hexagonal Prism (Figs. 2·12 and 2·13)

Set out the true profile of the hexagon 1, 2, 3, 4, 5, 6, to a convenient scale (Fig. 2·12). Draw the containing rectangle ABCD. Draw the isometric view of the rectangle $A^1B^1C^1D^1$ (Fig. 2·13). All lines depicting this rectangle are Isometric Lines and *measurements may only be set off along these lines—or along lines parallel to them.*

Mark off A^11^1=A1; A^16^1=A6—Join 1^16^1.
Mark off B^12^1=B2; B^13^1=B3—Join 1^12^1 and 2^13^1.
Mark off C^14^1=C4; D^15^1=D5—Join $3^14^15^1$ and 5^16^1.

Set off thickness T^1=T at 30 degrees to the horizontal and complete the view by means of lines parallel to the edges already drawn.

Choice of Position

Figs. 2·14 and 2·15 illustrate two alternative Isometric Views which could be drawn. These alternatives should always be considered and if they present a more comprehensive view of the object, one of them should be adopted.

Hidden detail is usually excluded from isometric views because it tends to destroy the "picture" value of the view.

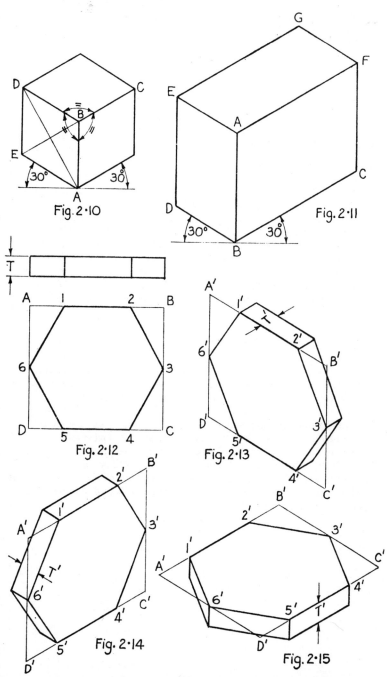

D   C
B
E
30°   30°
A
Fig. 2·10

G
F
E
A
C
D
30°   30°
B
Fig. 2·11

T

A   1   2   B

6   3

D   5   4   C
Fig. 2·12

A'
1'
T
2'
6'   B'
D'
5'   3'
4'   C'
Fig. 2·13

2'   B'
A' 1'
3'
T'
6'   C'
4'
D' 5'
Fig. 2·14

B'
2'   3'
A' 1'   C'
6'   5'   4'
T'
D'
Fig. 2·15

98

ISOMETRIC CURVES

The Isometric View of a Circle (Figs. 2·16, 2·17 and 2·18)

Draw the true shape of the circle to a convenient scale (Fig. 2·16).

Draw the containing square ABCD and then set the isometric view of the square $A^1B^1C^1D^1$ (Fig. 2·17). Mark off a series of vertical lines 1·1, 2·2, 3·3, etc. Reproduce these lines on the isometric view so that $A^11^1 = A1$, $A2^1 = A2$, etc. The line 1·1 cuts the circle at a and b. On the isometric view mark off along 1^11^1. $1^1a^1 = 1a$ and $1^1b^1 = 1b$. Along 2^12^1 mark off $2^1c^1 = 2c$ and $2^1d^1 = 2d$ and so on. Draw a smooth curve to pass through the points $a^1b^1c^1d^1$, etc. The completed ellipse is an isometric view of the given circle. (Another isometric view is shown at Fig. 2·18 and its construction is identical with that described.) Reference to Figs. 2·16, 2·17 and 2·18 will show that the construction could have been equally well carried out by means of horizontal divisions such as ff.

The Isometric View for any Curve

Two orthographic views of a solid are shown at Fig. 2·19 and an isometric view of it is illustrated at Fig. 2·20. The method of construction is self-explanatory and a close study will reveal that exactly the same method is used as for the isometric view of the circle described above.

Because hidden detail is seldom required on isometric views, time can be saved by first drawing the face nearest the observer's eye, since this face is completely visible. Then the face that is one stage further away is drawn and so on. The order of drawing is shown at Fig. 2·20, the face 1 being dealt with first, then 2, and 3 and finally 4. The curves at 1 and 3 are constructed, but those at 2 and 4 are merely set off from 1 and 3 by marking off the thickness of the feature along vertical lines drawn through selected points on 1 and 3.

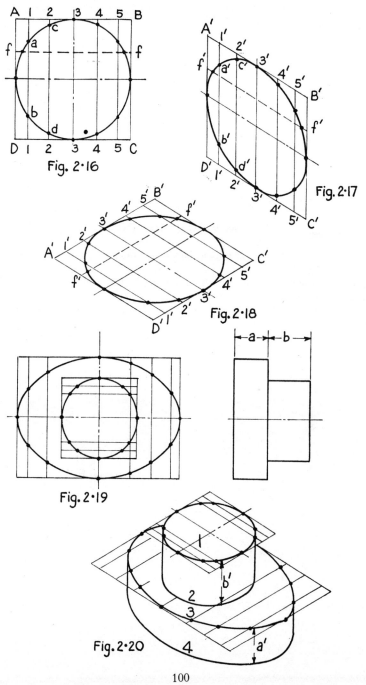

Fig. 2·16

Fig. 2·17

Fig. 2·18

Fig. 2·19

Fig. 2·20

100

ISOMETRIC PROJECTION

Problem Assignments

For convenience, the text of the questions in this section has been set at the bottom of the diagram sheets.

The twelve problems are progressive and should therefore be tackled in the order set.

The first six problems involve plane surfaces and the remainder curves.

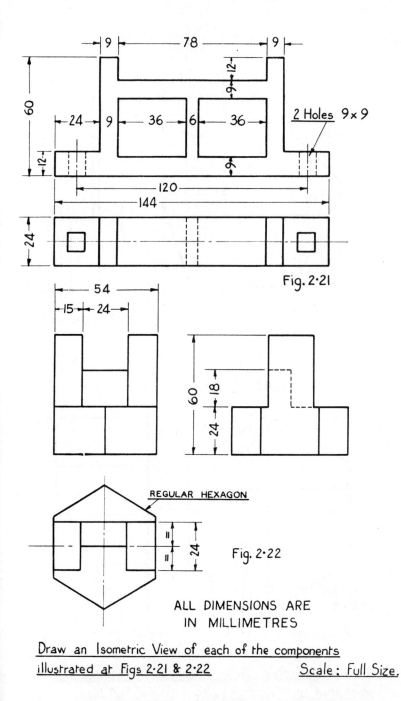

Fig. 2·21

2 Holes 9 × 9

REGULAR HEXAGON

Fig. 2·22

ALL DIMENSIONS ARE
IN MILLIMETRES

Draw an Isometric View of each of the components
illustrated at Figs 2·21 & 2·22   Scale: Full Size.

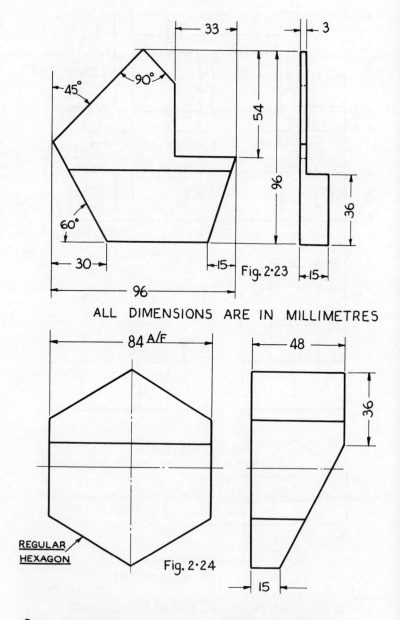

33

3

45°

90°

54

96

60°

30

15

Fig. 2·23

15

36

96

ALL DIMENSIONS ARE IN MILLIMETRES

84 A/F

48

36

REGULAR
HEXAGON

Fig. 2·24

15

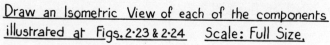

Draw an Isometric View of each of the components
illustrated at Figs. 2·23 & 2·24   Scale: Full Size.

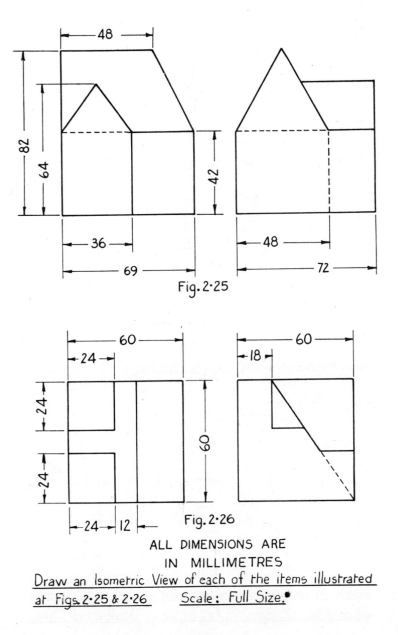

48

82

64

36

69

42

Fig. 2·25

48

72

60

24

24

24

24

12

60

60

18

Fig. 2·26

ALL DIMENSIONS ARE
IN MILLIMETRES

Draw an Isometric View of each of the items illustrated
at Figs. 2·25 & 2·26   Scale: Full Size.

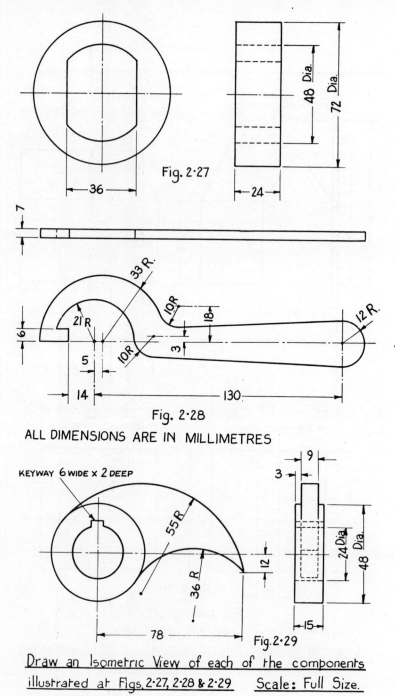

Fig. 2·27

48 Dia.

72 Dia.

36

24

7

33 R.

10R

18

21 R

10R

3

12 R.

5

14

130

Fig. 2·28

ALL DIMENSIONS ARE IN MILLIMETRES

KEYWAY 6 WIDE × 2 DEEP

55 R

3

9

24 Dia.

48 Dia.

12

36 R

78

15

Fig. 2·29

Draw an Isometric View of each of the components
illustrated at Figs. 2·27, 2·28 & 2·29   Scale: Full Size.

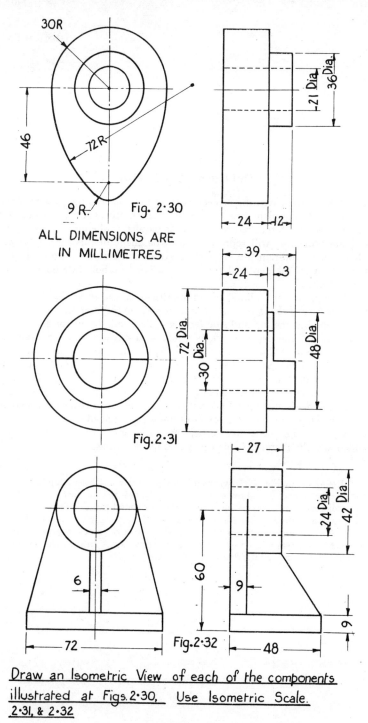

30R

72R

9 R.   Fig. 2·30

46

ALL DIMENSIONS ARE
IN MILLIMETRES

21 Dia.   36 Dia.

24   12

39

24   3

72 Dia.   48 Dia.

30

Fig. 2·31

27

24 Dia.   42 Dia.

60

9

6

9

72   Fig. 2·32   48

Draw an Isometric View of each of the components
illustrated at Figs. 2·30,   Use Isometric Scale.
2·31, & 2·32

OBLIQUE PROJECTION

In Oblique Projection the projectors from the object to the picture plane are *oblique* to the plane but are parallel to each other. If the object is set in a position such that one of its faces is parallel to the picture plane, the oblique projectors will reproduce the true shape of this face upon the plane. If, in addition, the projectors are inclined at 45* degrees to the picture plane, the depth of the object is not foreshortened on the projected view.

The majority of Oblique Views are drawn as shown at Fig. 2·36, viz. the *front face of the object and all faces parallel to the front face* retain their true shape but the top and side faces are distorted. $\theta = 30°$ or 45°.

There are, however, occasions when it is advantageous to draw an Oblique View as illustrated at Fig. 2·37, viz. the *top face and all faces parallel to the top face* retain their true shape but the front and side faces are distorted. This position is often used by builders and architects to show an aerial view of a building with the roof removed to expose the interior. This is shown at Fig. 2·38. It is convenient because the Orthographic plan of the building rotated through an angle of 45 degrees forms the top face. The necessary vertical lines showing depths can be readily added and the Pictorial View easily and quickly drawn.

* Reference to Fig. 2·33, where an Oblique View has been projected upon the Vertical Plane, will show that in order to reveal the top face of the object the projectors must also be inclined to the horizontal plane. This angle may be varied as desired. The effect of varying it is seen clearly at Figs. 2·34 and 2·35, A small angle of inclination brings the side of the block into prominence whereas a large angle shows the top face to advantage. In practice, angle θ is usually made either 30 degrees or 45 degrees.

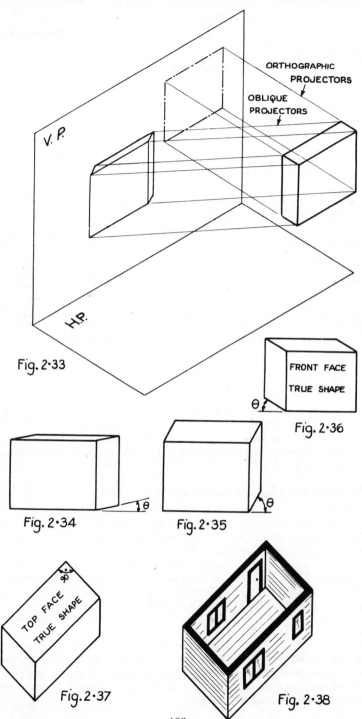

ORTHOGRAPHIC PROJECTORS

OBLIQUE PROJECTORS

V. P.

H.P.

Fig. 2·33

FRONT FACE TRUE SHAPE

θ

Fig. 2·36

Fig. 2·34

θ

Fig. 2·35

θ

TOP FACE TRUE SHAPE

90

Fig. 2·37

Fig. 2·38

108

OBLIQUE VIEWS

Fig. 2·39 shows an Oblique View of a rectangular block. AD, AC and AB are the Axes of projection. On the *top* and *bottom* face all measurements must be made along lines parallel to AD and AC. On the *side* faces all measurements must be set off along lines parallel to AC and AB. The *front* and *back* faces record the true shape and therefore measurements are not so confined. The angle θ is arbitrary, but for practical purposes is usually made either 30 or 45 degrees as previously stated.

To draw an Oblique View of a Rectangular Block 75 mm × 50 mm × 40 mm high (Fig. 2·40)

Draw ABCD to represent the true shape of the front face BD=75 mm AB=40 mm and angle ABD=90 degrees. Set off along lines drawn at 30 degrees to the horizontal BE and AF=50 mm. Complete the view by drawing FG, GC and FE parallel to AC, AF and AB respectively.

If a circle were drawn on each visible face of the block, then on the oblique view the circle on the front face would retain its true shape but on the top and side faces would become elliptical. This is shown at Fig. 2·40. It is therefore advisable when drawing oblique views to arrange, if possible, for any circular parts to appear either on the front face or on faces parallel to the front face.

To draw an Oblique View of a Cylinder 50 mm diameter × 25 mm long (Fig. 2·41)

This is readily drawn by selecting one of the circular ends as the front face of the view. Draw a 50 mm diameter circle with centre O. Set out the axis OP at 30 degrees to the horizontal and 25 mm long. P is the centre of the circle representing the back face. Join the two circles by tangents parallel to OP.

Treatment of Inclined Surfaces (Figs. 2·42 and 2·43)

The method of dealing with lines which are not parallel to the axes of projection when circumstances compel these lines to be drawn on the top face is illustrated at Figs. 2·42 and 2·43. The diagram is self-explanatory and it will be seen that the method adopted is similar to that used for isometric views. An undesirable feature of oblique projection is the distortion of the side and top faces and this is particularly noticeable at Fig. 2·43. This can be overcome by drawing all 30-degree lines to a different scale from that used for horizontal and vertical lines. In practice, however, one scale is usually adopted for quickness and the distortion is accepted.

In American practice oblique projection drawn to one scale only is sometimes referred to as Cavalier Projection, but if two scales are used (i.e. if the depths are foreshortened) the projection is known as Cabinet Projection. In English practice, however, it is unusual for any such distinction to be made.

109

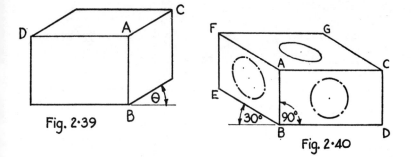

Fig. 2·39

Fig. 2·40

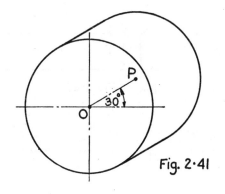

Fig. 2·41

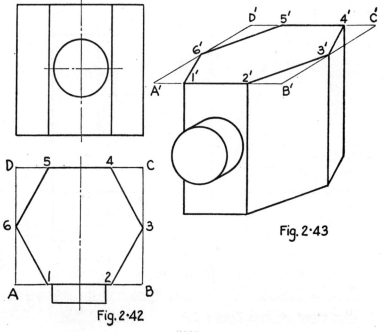

Fig. 2·43

Fig. 2·42

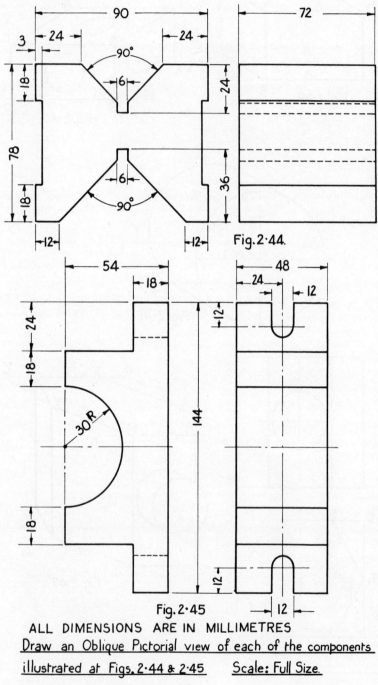

Fig. 2·44.

Fig. 2·45

ALL DIMENSIONS ARE IN MILLIMETRES

<u>Draw an Oblique Pictorial view of each of the components</u>

<u>illustrated at Figs. 2·44 & 2·45</u>   <u>Scale: Full Size.</u>

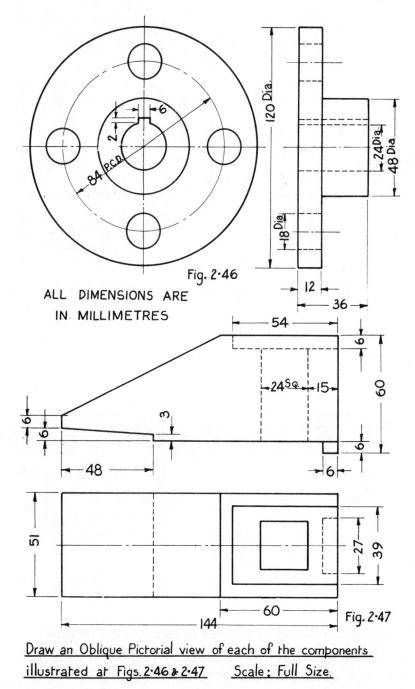

Fig. 2·46

ALL DIMENSIONS ARE
IN MILLIMETRES

Fig. 2·47

Draw an Oblique Pictorial view of each of the components
illustrated at Figs. 2·46 & 2·47   Scale: Full Size.

112

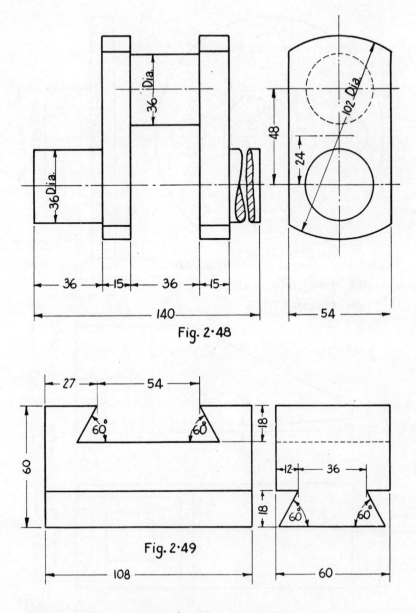

Fig. 2·48

Fig. 2·49

Draw an Oblique Pictorial view of each of the components
illustrated at Figs. 2·48 & 2·49   Scale: Full Size.

ALL DIMENSIONS ARE IN MILLIMETRES

113

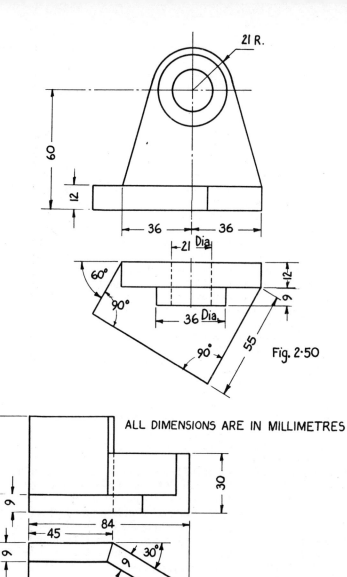

21 R.

60

12

36   36

21 Dia.

60°
90°

36 Dia.

12

9

90°

55

Fig. 2·50

ALL DIMENSIONS ARE IN MILLIMETRES

48

30

9

84

45

9

30°

9

48

60

Fig. 2·51

Draw an Oblique Pictorial view of each of the components
illustrated at Figs. 2·50 & 2·51 Scale: Full Size.

SKETCHING

Introduction

A sketch may be defined as a drawing in which the proportions are judged by eye. Sketches are sometimes produced with the aid of a straight edge and compass (to give good linework) and are then often referred to as Guided Sketches (see Fig. 3·1) to distinguish them from Freehand Sketches (see Fig. 3·2), in which all lines are drawn freehand. In preparing a sketch it is permissible to use either Pictorial or Orthographic projection, the type used depending upon the purpose for which the sketch is intended. All the rules and conventions appertaining to Pictorial and Orthographical views apply as rigidly to sketching as to drawing. A sketch can be produced far quicker than a scale drawing, and in the case of a freehand sketch can be prepared "on the spot" since the only equipment needed is a pencil and paper.

Sketching ability is a great asset to the engineer because it will enable him to clarify an explanation, convey an instruction, or express an idea. In practice, the majority of new ideas are initially expressed in the form of sketches which are subsequently converted into scale drawings. Many students approach the subject of sketching with certain misgivings. The authors would like, therefore, to emphasize here that in their experience the simple skills required to produce an Engineering Sketch are within the reach of any student who is prepared to exercise a little patience and perseverance.

There are three skills that the beginner must acquire: (1) an "eye" for proportion; (2) the ability to draw freehand a reasonably straight line; (3) the ability to draw freehand a reasonable circle.

The best results are obtained if each skill is acquired separately. Thus by commencing with Guided Sketching the beginner is able to concentrate entirely on developing an eye for proportion. Having mastered this, problems on freehand sketching involving only straight lines enable the second skill to be acquired. Finally, problems involving circles and curves complete the basic training.

Practice makes perfect, and the beginner having completed the basic training should sketch at every possible opportunity.

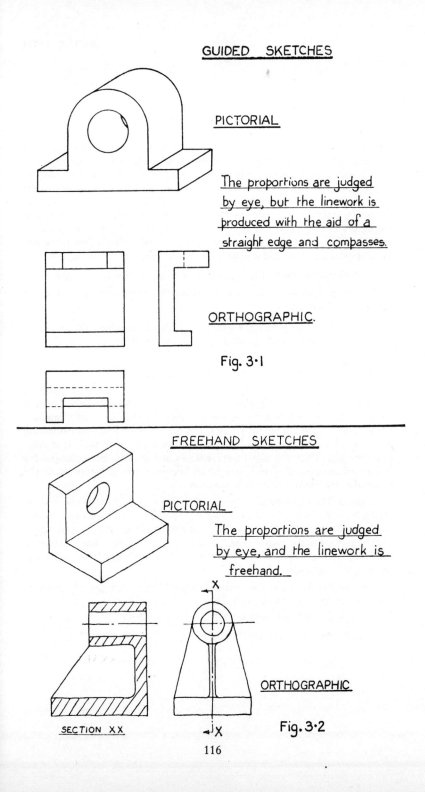

GUIDED SKETCHES

PICTORIAL

The proportions are judged by eye, but the linework is produced with the aid of a straight edge and compasses.

ORTHOGRAPHIC.

Fig. 3·1

FREEHAND SKETCHES

PICTORIAL

The proportions are judged by eye, and the linework is freehand.

X

ORTHOGRAPHIC

SECTION XX

X

Fig. 3·2

116

GUIDED SKETCHES

The dimensions of a guided sketch are judged by eye. A set square or straight edge is used to guide the pencil when drawing straight lines; circles and arcs are drawn with the aid of compasses. *The finished linework is of the same quality as that of a scale drawing.* Because its proportions are estimated and not accurately measured, a guided sketch should be produced in roughly one-half the time taken to prepare a scale drawing. Beginners often spend too much time on a sketch by trying to obtain scale drawing accuracy—without the use of a scale. The following points are important and should always be borne in mind when sketching:

(1) A sketch is essentially a *quick* method of representing shape.

(2) The proportions of a sketch should be *reasonable*—they are not expected to be *exact*.

It is proposed to prepare a guided sketch of the block illustrated at Fig. 3·3. The front elevation and the end view will be sketched.

Order of Procedure

1. *Establish the Overall Proportions of the Block* (Fig. 3·4). Judged by eye, the overall length is approximately twice the overall height. Using a straight edge as guide draw a rectangle *abcd* such that $ab = 2ad$ (approx.). The overall height is roughly three times the overall thickness. Projecting the overall height from *abcd*, draw a second rectangle *adef* such that $ad = 3ed$ (approx.). Turn the paper upside down and inspect the rectangles for squareness and parallelism (these faults become more apparent when the rectangles are viewed from this position).

2. *Insert Main Centre Lines* (Fig. 3·5). The vertical centre line divides *abcd* into approximately two equal parts ($dl = lc$). The horizontal centre line is positioned at about two-thirds of the height above the base ($ag = 2gd$). Again turn the paper round and inspect the centre lines to ensure that they are approximately square with each other and parallel to the sides of the rectangle.

3. Draw faintly, fill in the outlines of the block estimating the proportions as before, e.g. $lh = hc$; $ck = 2kb$, etc. (Fig. 3·6).

4. Clean up and line in (Fig. 3·7).

5. Add Dimension and TITLE, state clearly "NOT TO SCALE".

117

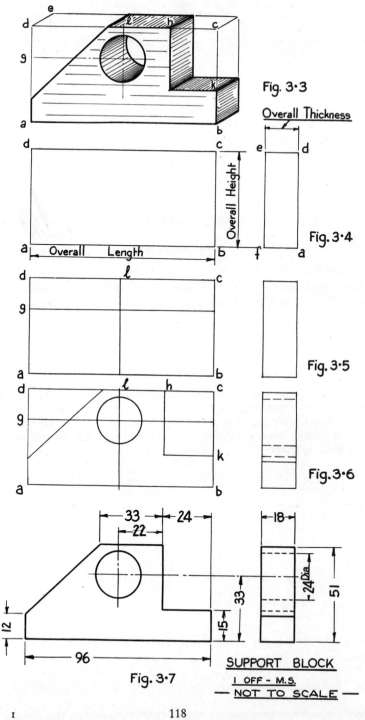

e d

Fig. 3·3

Overall Thickness

Fig. 3·4

Overall Height

Overall Length

Fig. 3·5

Fig. 3·6

33 24

22

18

24 Dia. 51

33

15

12

96

Fig. 3·7

<u>SUPPORT BLOCK</u>
<u>1 OFF – M.S.</u>
– <u>NOT TO SCALE</u> –

I

118

GUIDED SKETCHING

Problem Assignments

Exercise 1

Sketch the Front Elevation, End View and Plan of the block illustrated at Fig. 3·8. First or Third Angle Orthographic Projection may be used.

Exercise 2

Sketch an Isometric View of the Slide Base shown at Fig. 3·9.

NOTE

When sketching a pictorial view of an object, establish the overall proportions by sketching first the pictorial view of the box or crate which would just contain the object, then proceed as previously described.

The solution to each question should occupy a space of approximately 375 mm × 275 mm.

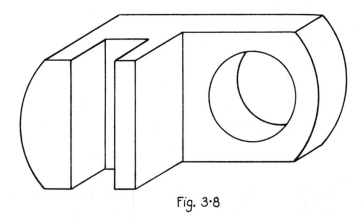

Fig. 3·8

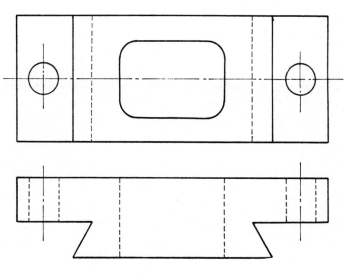

Fig. 3·9

GUIDED SKETCHING

Problem Assignments

Exercise 3

Sketch a Half Sectional Elevation and End View of the Casing shown at Fig. 3·10. First or Third Angle Projection may be used.

Exercise 4

Using either First or Third Angle Projection, sketch the following views of the Crank Lever illustrated at Fig. 3·11:

(1) The Front Elevation as given.

(2) A Sectional End View—the plane of section being indicated by the line XX.

(3) A Plan looking in the direction of the Arrow B.

Note

The solution to each problem should occupy a space of approximately 375 mm × 275 mm.

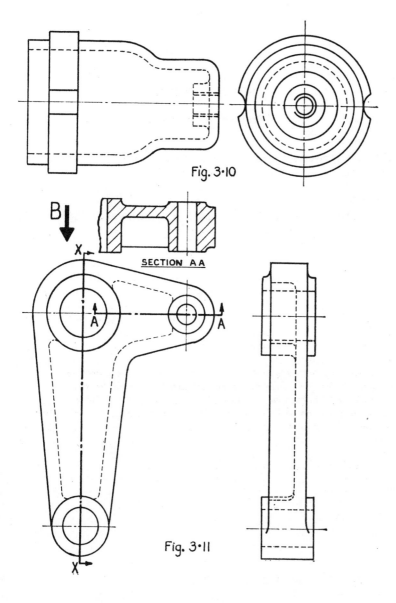

Fig. 3·10

SECTION A A

B

X

A A

X

Fig. 3·11

122

GUIDED SKETCHING

Problem Assignments

Exercise 5

Sketch the given sectional view of the Cottered Joint illustrated at Fig. 3·12.

Exercise 6

Sketch the given views of the Stuffing Box Assembly shown at Fig. 3·13.

NOTES

The function of a Cotter* is to prevent relative axial movement between mating parts. As a fastening it was universally used in the early days of engineering, but the introduction of screwed fastenings has limited its use in modern practice. There are still, however, special applications where it is preferred. Long tie-rods and rods for pumps are often made in sections which are jointed together by means of cotters, and it is still standard practice to fasten the pedal crank of a bicycle to its shaft by means of a cotter pin.

A stuffing box is a leak-proof housing. It allows a rod or shaft to rotate or to move axially but prevents liquid or gas under pressure from leaking past the moving surfaces. The gland is clamped tightly by means of studs and nuts and thus exerts a pressure on the packing ring (which is usually made of asbestos) forcing it hard against the surface of the rod or shaft.

*It should be noted that a cotter pin (as distinct from a cotter of the type illustrated at Fig. 3·12) will prevent rotary, as well as axial, movement between mating parts.

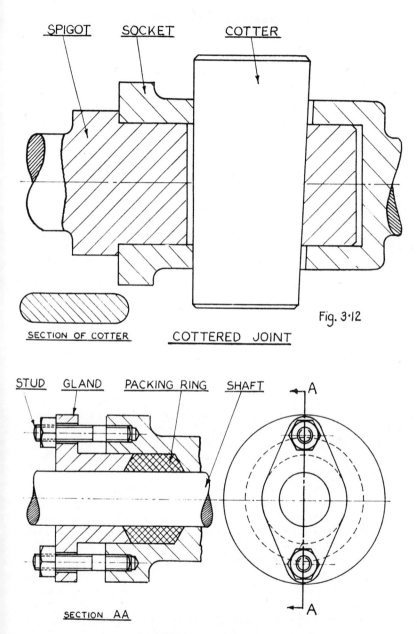

SPIGOT   SOCKET   COTTER

SECTION OF COTTER   COTTERED JOINT   Fig. 3·12

STUD GLAND   PACKING RING   SHAFT   A

SECTION AA

STUFFING BOX

Fig. 3·13

124

FREEHAND SKETCHES

A freehand sketch is produced *without* the aid of a straight edge or compass and the proportions are judged by eye. The lines are drawn with a soft pencil, and an HB or F grade is recommended for this purpose.

It is accepted that the finished linework or a freehand sketch is inferior to that of a scale drawing or a guided sketch. The order of procedure is the same for a freehand sketch as for a guided sketch, i.e. the overall proportions established, then the positions of the main centre lines are fixed and finally the outline is inserted; the sketch is then checked, cleaned up and lined in. Before tackling a freehand sketch, however, the beginner must learn to draw his lines freehand. Lines fall into one of two categories, they are either straight or curved, and the student is advised to master the art of drawing straight lines before proceding to the rather more difficult task of drawing curves.

The exercises shown on the opposite page (Figs. 3·14 to 3·28) will, if practised diligently, enable the beginner to acquire a reasonable degree of skill in sketching straight lines. These are BASIC graded exercises and it is important that they are tackled in chronological order. Each exercise should be mastered before proceeding to the next one.

Exercises

Fig. 3·14. Sketch a series of vertical lines about 100 mm long and spaced approximately 12 mm apart.

Fig. 3·15. Sketch a series of horizontal lines about 100 mm long and spaced approximately 12 mm apart.

Figs. 3·16 and 3·17. Sketch two series of parallel inclined· lines about 130 mm long and 5 mm apart. The lines to be inclined at 60 degrees to the horizontal.

Figs. 3·18, 3·19, 3·20 and 3·21. Sketch four series of right angles, the lengths of the sides being approximately 50 mm.

Figs. 3·22, 3·23, 3·24 and 3·25. Sketch four right-angled triangles. ABC=60 degrees approximately and the base length to be about 80 mm in length.

Fig. 3·26. Sketch a rectangle approximately 150 mm × 75 mm.

Fig. 3·27. Sketch a square of approximately 75 mm side.

Fig. 3·28. *Test Piece.* Sketch a square having sides approximately 100 mm long and insert the bisectors of all sides and angles. The bisectors should intersect at one point which is the centroid of the square.

NOTE

The general "straightness" of the lines is more important than a high degree of finish. If the lines are produced by means of a series of short strokes (which is usual in sketching), they will have a "feathery" appearance which is quite acceptable. Sketch the lines faintly and then line in after checking for straightness and direction.

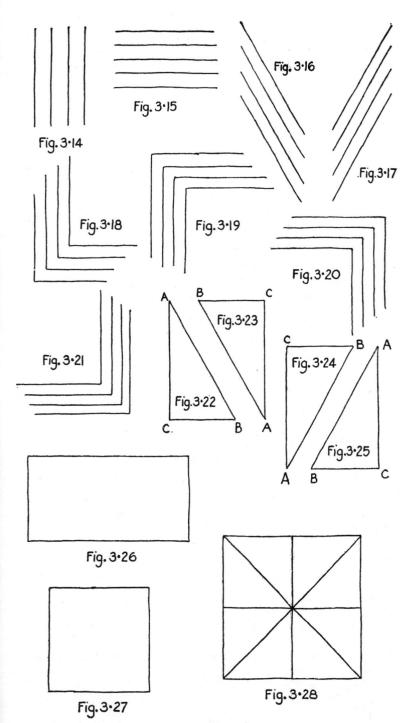

Fig. 3·14

Fig. 3·15

Fig. 3·16

Fig. 3·17

Fig. 3·18

Fig. 3·19

Fig. 3·20

Fig. 3·21

Fig. 3·22

Fig. 3·23

Fig. 3·24

Fig. 3·25

Fig. 3·26

Fig. 3·27

Fig. 3·28

FREEHAND SKETCHING (CURVES)

Having attained a reasonable degree of skill in sketching straight lines, the beginner must now learn to sketch curves. The basic exercises (Figs. 3·29 to 3·35) set out on the opposite page should be attempted in chronological order and each exercise should be thoroughly mastered before proceeding to the next.

Curves must always be sketched from the INSIDE and never from the outside. For instance, Fig. 3·29 should be sketched with the paper the right way up, but it is necessary to turn the paper upside down in order to sketch Fig. 3·30. For this reason the sketch paper should *not* be fastened to a drawing board.

Curves should be sketched with short strokes of the pencil giving a "feathery" outline but one whose "direction" is true. *Until a high degree of skill has been acquired it will usually be necessary to correct the first attempt* when sketching curves and circles.

Exercise 1 (Fig. 3·29)

Select 5 points A, B, C, D and E, the distance between adjacent points being approximately 25 mm. Sketch a smooth curve to pass through all points.

Exercise 2 (Fig. 3·30)

Select 5 points F, G, H, J and K, the distance between adjacent points being approximately 25 mm. Sketch a smooth curve to pass through all points.

Exercise 3 (Fig. 3·31)

Sketch an "ogee" curve AB=BC=60 mm approximately.

*Exercise 4 (Fig. 3·33)

Sketch a small circle (approximately 20 mm diameter).

*Exercise 5 (Fig. 3·35)

Sketch a large circle (approximately 80 mm diameter).

*Hints on sketching Circles

(*a*) Small Circles (up to 25 mm diameter approximately). Sketch a vertical and a horizontal line to intersect at O (see Fig. 3·32). Judging the distance by eye, set off O1=O2=O3=O4=radius of arc. Sketch in the semicircle to pass through 4, 1, and 2. Turn the paper upside down and draw the other semicircle to pass through 2, 3 and 4. Inspect and if necessary correct the completed circle (see Fig. 3·33). Clean up and line in.

(*b*) Large Circles (greater than 25 mm diameter). Sketch a vertical and a horizontal line to intersect at O (see Fig. 3·34). Sketch the bisectors of the four right angles. Judging the distances by eye set out O1=O2=O3, etc.=radius of circle. Proceed as for small circle, and produce finished circle as shown at Fig. 3·35.

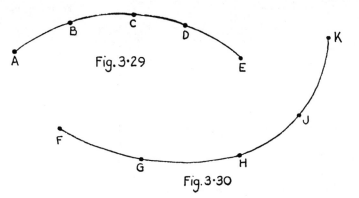

Fig. 3·29

Fig. 3·30

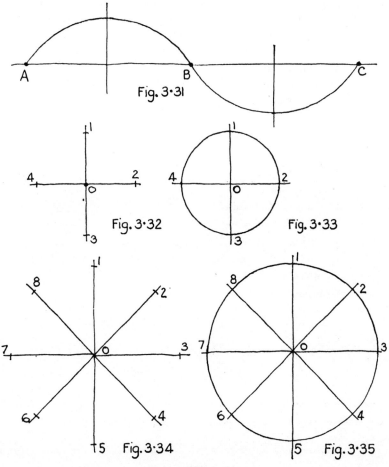

Fig. 3·31

Fig. 3·32

Fig. 3·33

Fig. 3·34

Fig. 3·35

FREEHAND SKETCHING

Problem Assignments

In the following problem assignments the student is expected to obtain his own models (or illustrations) for each of the parts to be sketched.

Sketch freehand and in good proportion two orthographic views (or one pictorial view) of each of the items listed below. Sketches should be of reasonable size and should occupy a space of approximately 275 mm × 375 mm.

(1) A Double Ended Spanner.

(2) A Pair of Outside Calipers.

(3) The Crank of a Pedal Cycle (with pedal removed).

(4) A pair of Pencil Springbows.

(5) A Stanchion Base.

(6) A Stanchion Cap.

(7) A Beam Compass.

(8) A Chuck Key.

(9) A pair of Pliers.

(10) A "Stauffer" Lubricator.

(11) A Taper Roller Bearing.

(12) A Ball Journal Bearing.

(13) A Simple Non-Return Valve.

(14) A Lathe Carrier.

(15) A Machine Vice.

PART II

GEOMETRICAL DRAWING

Comprising

130

GEOMETRICAL CONSTRUCTIONS

Bisectors and Perpendiculars

Introduction

It is now widely accepted that in teaching Engineering Drawing the students' attention should be directed towards acquiring an ability to think in three dimensions rather than to concentrate upon the mere craft of draughtsmanship. The authors also believe it is better to build the teaching programme round the theory of projection and not upon the solution of obtuse geometrical problems. In this text-book, therefore, geometry is regarded as an auxiliary subject and the examples now discussed, without proof, are a brief resumé of the geometrical constructions that arise in the preparation of Machine Drawings.

Example 1. *To bisect a given line AB* (Fig. 4·1)

With A as centre and a radius approximately equal to AB, describe an arc above and below AB. With B as centre, describe similar arcs to cut the first at points P and Q. Join PQ to bisect AB at C.

Note.—PQ will also be perpendicular to the given line AB.

Example 2. *To draw a line perpendicular to a given line AB, through a given point C* (Fig. 4·2)

With C as centre and any suitable radius, describe equal arcs to cut AB at points D and E. With D as centre and radius DE, describe an arc above (or below) AB. With E as centre, describe a similar arc to cut the first at F. The line CF will be perpendicular to AB.

Example 3. *Alternative construction for Example* 2 (Fig. 4·3)

With C as centre and any suitable radius, describe an arc to cut AB at D. With D as centre and radius CD, cut the arc at E, and with E as centre and the same radius, cut the arc again at F. With E and F as centres, describe equal arcs to intersect at G. The line CG will be perpendicular to the given line AB.

Example 4. *To find the centre of a given circle* (Fig. 4·4)

Draw any two chords to the circle, such as AB and CD, and bisect these at right angles as shown in Example 1. The two perpendicular bisectors will intersect at O, the centre of the circle.

Example 5. *To describe a circle to pass through three given points: A, B and C* (Fig. 4·5)

Join AB and BC and bisect both lines at right angles. The intersection O of the perpendicular bisectors is the centre of the required circle and its radius is AO, BO or CO.

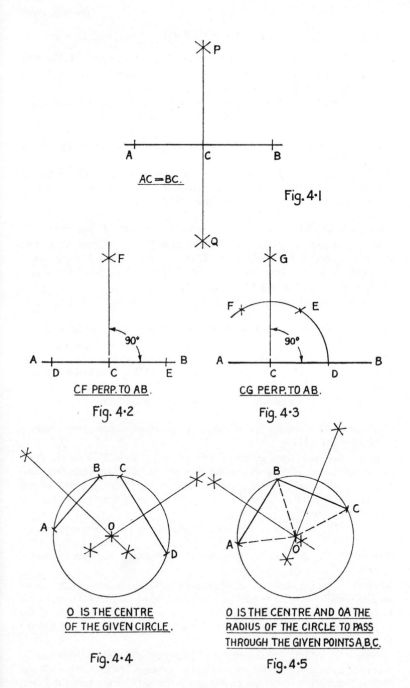

P

A ———|——— C ——————— B

AC = BC.

Fig. 4·1

Q

F

90°

A ——|———— C ———— B
    D   E

CF PERP. TO AB.

Fig. 4·2

G

F   E

90°

A ———— C ———— D ———— B

CG PERP. TO AB.

Fig. 4·3

B C

A

O

D

O IS THE CENTRE
OF THE GIVEN CIRCLE.

Fig. 4·4

B

A

O

C

O IS THE CENTRE AND OA THE
RADIUS OF THE CIRCLE TO PASS
THROUGH THE GIVEN POINTS A,B,C.

Fig. 4·5

132

TANGENCY (1)

Example 1. *To draw a tangent to a given circle from a given point P* (Fig. 4·6)

Find the centre O of the given circle and join PO. Draw PQ perpendicular to PO. PQ is the tangent to the circle at point P.

Note.—PO is called the normal; the tangent and normal at any point on a curve are always perpendicular to each other.

Example 2. *To draw a tangent to a circle from a point P that is outside the given circle* (Fig. 4·7)

Find the centre O of the given circle and join PO. Bisect OP at Q and describe a semicircle on OP to cut the given circle at T. TP is the required tangent and OT the normal at the point T.

Example 3. *To draw a tangent to two given circles—case I* (Fig. 4·8)

With O_2 as centre, draw a circle of radius $R_2 - R_1$. Bisect O_1O_2 and describe a semicircle on O_1O_2 to cut this circle at T. Join O_2T and produce to cut the larger of given circles at point T_2. Draw O_1T_1 parallel to O_2T_2. T_1T_2 is the required tangent.

Note.—The corresponding tangent for an "open-belt" drive is T_3T_4.

Example 4. *To draw a tangent to two given circles—case II* (Fig. 4·9)

With O_2 as centre, draw an arc of radius $R_2 + R_1$. Bisect O_1O_2 and describe a semicircle on O_1O_2 to cut this arc at T. Join O_2T to cut the larger of given circles at point T_2. Draw O_1T_1 parallel to O_2T_2. T_1T_2 is the required tangent.

Note.—The corresponding tangent for a "crossed-belt" drive is T_3T_4.

Example 5. *To draw an arc of radius R tangential to two given circles— case I* (Fig. 4·10)

With O_1 as centre, draw an arc of radius $R - R_1$. With O_2 as centre, draw an arc of radius $R - R_2$ to cut the first arc at point O. Join OO_1 and produce to T_1 and join OO_2 and produce to T_2. O is the centre of the required tangential arc, and T_1 and T_2 the points of tangency of the arc to the given circles.

Note.—T_3 and T_4 are the points of tangency of the alternative arc.

Example 6. *To draw an arc of radius R tangential to two given circles— case II* (Fig. 4·11)

With O_1 as centre, draw an arc of radius $R + R_1$. With O_2 as centre, draw an arc of radius $R + R_2$ to cut the first arc at point O. Join OO_1 and OO_2 to cut the given circles at T_1 and T_2 respectively. O is the centre of the required tangential arc and T_1 and T_2 the points of tangency of the arc to the given circles.

Note.—T_3 and T_4 are the points of tangency of the alternative arc. In Example 5 the given circles are said to be "internal" to the tangential arc, and in Example 6 the given circles are "external" to the tangential arc.

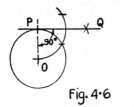

Fig. 4·6

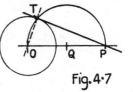

Fig. 4·7

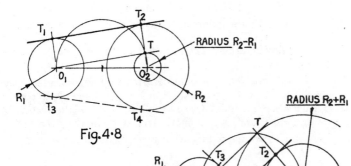

RADIUS R_2-R_1

Fig. 4·8

RADIUS R_2+R_1

Fig. 4·9

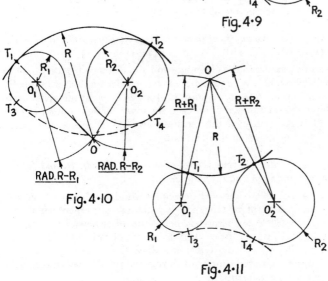

RAD. $R-R_1$

RAD. $R-R_2$

Fig. 4·10

$R+R_1$

$R+R_2$

R

Fig. 4·11

TANGENCY (2)

Example 1. To draw an arc of radius R tangential to two given circles—case III (Fig. 4·12)

With O_1 as centre, draw an arc of radius $R-R_1$. With O_2 as centre, draw an arc of radius $R+R_2$ to cut the first arc at point O. Join OO_1 and produce to T_1. Join OO_2 to cut the larger given circle at T_2. O is the centre of the required arc and T_1 and T_2 its points of tangency with the given circles.

Note.—T_3 and T_4 are the points of tangency of the alternative arc.

Example 2. To draw an arc of radius R tangential to two given circles—case IV (Fig. 4·13)

With O_1 as centre, draw an arc of radius $R+R_1$. With O_2 as centre, draw an arc of radius $R-R_2$ to cut the first arc at point O. Join OO_1 to cut the smaller given circle at T_1. Join OO_2 and produce to T_2. O is the centre of the required arc and T_1 and T_2 its points of tangency with the given circles.

Note.—T_3 and T_4 are the points of tangency of the alternative arc.

Example 3. To draw an arc of radius R tangential to two given lines (Fig. 4·14)

Draw two lines parallel to the given lines and at a distance from them equal to the radius R to intersect at point O. Perpendiculars from O will intersect the given lines at T_1 and T_2. O is the centre of the required arc and T_1 and T_2 the points of tangency with the given lines.

Example 4. To draw an arc of radius R tangential to a given line and a given arc (Fig. 4·15)

Draw a line parallel to the given line and at a distance from it equal to the radius R. From O_1 the centre of the given arc draw an arc of radius R_1+R to cut the parallel line at the point O. Join OO_1 to cut the given arc at T_1 and draw a perpendicular from O to the given straight line to intersect it at T. O is the centre of the required arc and T and T_1 the points of tangency with the given line and arc.

Example 5. To draw a reverse arc (ogee curve) of radii R_1 and R_2 to meet two given lines tangentially (Fig. 4·16)

Draw a line parallel to one of the given lines and at a distance from it equal to R_1. Assume point of tangency P and draw a perpendicular at P to obtain centre O_1. Draw a line parallel to the other given line at a distance from it equal to R_2 and from O_1 draw an arc of radius R_1+R_2 to cut the second parallel at O_2. Join O_1O_2 and draw the perpendicular O_2T_2. O_1 and O_2 are the required centres of the ogee curve that will meet at T_1 and touch given lines tangentially.

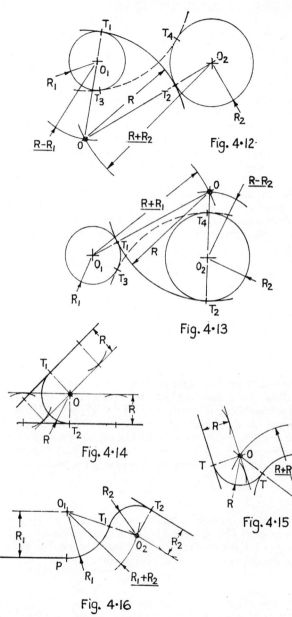

Fig. 4·12·

Fig. 4·13

Fig. 4·14

Fig. 4·15

Fig. 4·16

CONIC SECTIONS

In addition to the simple geometrical constructions already discussed there are a number of "Engineering Curves" that are of special interest and the first group of these to be reviewed are known as CONICS. These curves may be easily recognized when they are regarded as sections cut from a right circular cone, i.e. a cone whose axis is perpendicular to its circular base. Excluding the section plane that contains the axis of the cone, the four typical conic sections are those illustrated in Fig. 4·17— (a) *A Circle*, (b) *An Ellipse*, (c) *A Parabola* and (d) *A Hyperbola*. It should be noted that in case (*a*) the section plane is perpendicular to the axis of the cone, in case (*b*) it is inclined to the axis at an angle greater than the inclination of the sloping sides of the cone, in case (*c*) the section plane is parallel to the sloping sides and in case (*d*) the inclination with respect to the axis is less than that of the sloping sides. Where the dimensions of the cone and the position of the section plane are stated, the shape and size of the particular conic may be obtained by direct projection, as shown with a minimum of construction by the diagrams given in Figs. 4·18, 4·19, 4·20 and 4·21.

Circle

Little need be said of the conic section shown in Fig. 4·18; the diameter or radius of the circle is immediately obtained as soon as the actual section plane XX is reproduced in the elevation.

Ellipse

An examination of the outline of the section given in Fig. 4·19 reveals the fact that an ellipse has a changing diameter which varies between maximum and minimum values that are known as the *Major and Minor Axes*. Depending upon the dimensions of the cone and the inclination of the section plane, the ratio between the major and minor axes may vary very widely, but they are always perpendicular to one another. In contrast to the circle, the curvature of an ellipse is continually changing.

Parabola

The profile of the section in Fig. 4·20 shows that the *Parabola* has only one axis of symmetry. This axis is perpendicular to the base of the curve, and the highest point, the *vertex*, lies on this axis. The axial height of the curve may be greater or less than the base width.

Hyperbola

The *Hyperbola* shown in Fig. 4·21 is somewhat similar to a parabola; it has one axis of symmetry which is perpendicular to the base, and the vertex lies on this axis. The flanks of the curve are, however, noticably "flatter" than the flanks of a parabola.

137

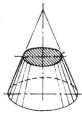

(a) CIRCLE.   (b) ELLIPSE.   (c) PARABOLA.   (d) HYPERBOLA.

Fig. 4·17

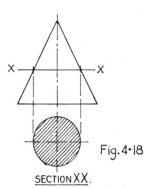

Fig. 4·18

SECTION XX.

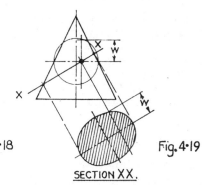

Fig. 4·19

SECTION XX.

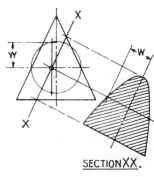

SECTION XX.

Fig. 4·20

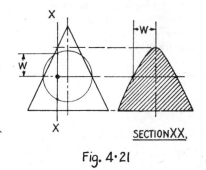

SECTION XX.

Fig. 4·21

138

ELLIPSE

Where the length of the axes are stated, one of the following constructions is generally used.

Rectangular Method (Fig. 4·22)

From the mid-point O of the major axis draw a perpendicular and mark off OC and OD each equal to half of the length of the minor axis CD. Draw EF and HG parallel with AB and EH and FG parallel with CD to obtain the rectangle EFGH. Divide AO into any number of equal parts and AE into the *same number* of equal parts—numbering the divisions from A as shown. Through these points draw radials from C and D to intersect at points on the required curve, as shown in the diagram.

The construction may be repeated for the other three quadrants, but a more rapid method is to transfer points as indicated in Fig. 4·22.

Auxiliary Circle Method (Fig. 4·23)

Draw the major and minor axes equally spaced about their point of intersection O. With centre O, describe two concentric circles, one with AB as diameter and the other with CD as diameter. Draw any radial through O to cut the two circles at E and F respectively. Draw a line through E parallel with AB, and a line through F parallel with CD; the intersection of these two lines is a point on the required ellipse. Additional radials through O will enable further points to be determined and by transferring these from one quaudrant to another the complete ellipse may be constructed.

Four Arc Approximate Ellipse (Fig. 4·24)

An approximate ellipse made up of circular arcs is often used for making the template for an elliptical arch. One method of construction is shown in Fig. 4·24. Having set out the major and minor axes, describe an arc with centre O and radius AO to intersect the minor axis produced at E. Join AC and mark off CF equal to CE. Bisect AF at right angles and produce the bisecting line to cut AB at G, and CD (or CD produced) at H. Mark off OJ equal to OG, and OK equal to OH. With centre G and radius AG draw an arc through A; with centre H and radius CH draw an arc through C. These two arcs will meet tangentially at the line bisecting AF. The approximate ellipse will be completed by describing similar arcs from the centres J and K.

Alternative Four Arc Curve (Fig. 4·25)

Construct the rectangle EFGH on the given axes and join ED. Bisect AE at J and join JC to intersect ED at K. The line bisecting AK will intersect AB at L and the line bisecting KC will intersect CD, or CD produced, at M. L and M are the centres of the circular arcs that will pass through A and C respectively and meet tangentially at K. By transferring L to P and M to N the corresponding centres may be obtained and the approximate, compass drawn, ellipse completed.

It should be noted that *any* method of construction that reduces the profile of an ellipse to a series of circular arcs is an approximation.

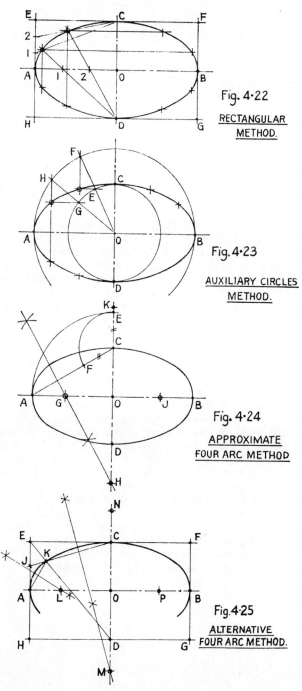

Fig. 4·22
RECTANGULAR
METHOD.

Fig. 4·23
AUXILIARY CIRCLES
METHOD.

Fig. 4·24
APPROXIMATE
FOUR ARC METHOD

Fig. 4·25
ALTERNATIVE
FOUR ARC METHOD.

140

PARABOLA

In practice the dimensions of a parabola are frequently given by stating the base width and the axial height, the two prime dimensions that in a bridge design are commonly referred to as the "span" and "rise" of the curve, and these two measurements indicate the size of the rectangle which will just contain or enclose the parabola.

Rectangular Construction

Fig. 4·26 shows a very common method of construction that is used when the dimensions of the enclosing rectangle are known. From the mid-point O of the base BC draw the perpendicular, mark off the axial height OA and complete the rectangle BCED. Divide AD into any number of equal parts, and DB into the *same number of equal parts*—in this instance four divisions have been chosen for both AD and DB, and the points of division are numbered as shown in Fig. 4·26. From the divisions in AD draw lines parallel with the axis AO and from the divisions in DB draw the radiating lines that all meet at A. The intersection of corresponding parallel and radiating lines give points on the required parabola. The curve may be completed by repeating the construction, or the points already determined may be transferred to the R.H. part of the containing rectangle as demonstrated in an earlier example.

Offset Construction

Given the "span" and "rise" of the parabola, the enclosing rectangle is first drawn, as shown in Fig. 4·27. From the mathematical properties of a parabola it is known that the abscissae are proportional to the square of their distances from the axis—i.e. *the offset distances from DE measured parallel with the axis AO are proportional to THE SQUARE of their distances from the axis AO.* Thus, by dividing DA into any convenient number of equal parts the offsets may be readily determined for each point of division. In Fig. 4·27 four divisions have been used so that $FA = \frac{1}{4}DA$: $GA = \frac{1}{2}DA$ and $HA = \frac{3}{4}DA$ and it follows that the offsets FF_1, GG_1 and HH_1 are respectively equal to $\frac{1}{16}AO$, $\frac{1}{4}AO$ and $\frac{9}{16}AO$. With DA divided into 4 divisions it is convenient to divide DB into 16 divisions. If DA is divided in 5 equal parts, DB should be divided into 25 equal parts, and the corresponding offset distances would be $\frac{1}{25} : \frac{4}{25} : \frac{9}{25}$ and $\frac{16}{25}$ of DB. The remaining half of the curve has been completed in the usual manner.

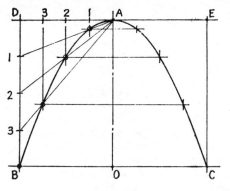

Fig. 4·26

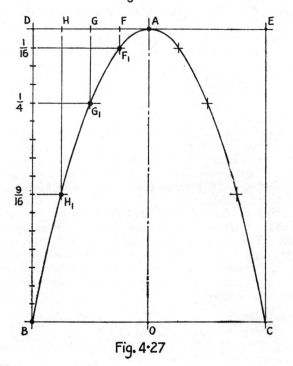

Fig. 4·27

HYPERBOLA

The rectangular hyperbola is of special interest to engineers because it indicates the behaviour of a gas when it is expanded or compressed. In Fig. 4·28 P is a point on a rectangular hyperbola, its actual position being given by the rectangular dimensions Px and Py, and P may be regarded as the point where the expansion of a gas commences.

Construction

Draw a line PM parallel with OX. From O draw any line OA_1 to cut PM at A_1 and Px at A_2. Through A_1 draw a line parallel with OY and through A_2 draw a line parallel with OX; the point of intersection A of these two lines will lie on the required curve. The line OB_2B_1 chosen quite at random will enable the point B to be determined, and additional points on the hyperbola may be obtained in a similar manner. Where it is necessary to produce the curve above the given point P draw PN parallel with OY and proceed in a similar manner, i.e. the random lines OC_2C_1 and OD_2D_1 will enable the points C and D to be determined.

The straight lines OX and OY may be regarded as rather special tangents that have no finite points of tangency—i.e. they finally touch or meet the curve at infinity. These two lines are given a special name—*Asymptotes*—and they may be inclined to one another at an angle greater or less than 90 degrees. Only in the case of a rectangular hyperbola are the asymptotes perpendicular.

The method of construction described above may be used for drawing any hyperbola providing the inclination of the asymptotes is known and the position of one point on the curve is given with reference to the asymptotes. Figs. 4·29 and 4·30 indicate the application of this method where the angle between the asymptotes is not 90 degrees. It should be noted that in all examples the generating lines drawn through P are *parallel to the asymptotes*.

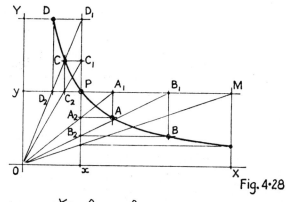

Fig. 4·28

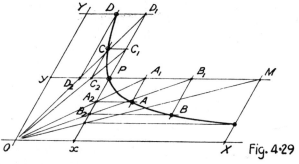

Fig. 4·29

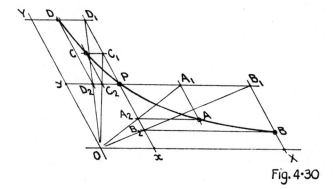

Fig. 4·30

144

CONIC SECTIONS—TANGENTS AND NORMALS

In practice it is often necessary to draw the tangent, or the normal, to a given curve, and in the following diagrams the methods of construction required to obtain these for the ellipse, parabola and hyperbola are shown.

Ellipse

Fig. 4·31 illustrates a true ellipse drawn with a major axis AB and a minor axis CD; the intersection of these axes is at O and it is required to draw a tangent to the curve at any point P which lies on the curve. With centre C and a radius AO strike arcs to cut the major axis at the points F_1 and F_2. Join F_1 to the point P and produce the line to Q. Join F_2 to P and bisect the angle F_2PQ. The bisector PR of the angle F_2PQ is the required tangent to the ellipse. The bisector of the angle F_2PF_1 will be the normal to the curve at the point P, PS and PR being perpendicular to one another. (F_1 and F_2 are called the Foci of the ellipse.)

Parabola

In Fig. 4·32 a parabola has been drawn having a base BC and an axial height AO. It is required to draw a tangent to the curve at any point such as P which lies on the curve. Draw PQ parallel to the base BC, i.e. perpendicular to the axis AO. On the axis produced mark off AR equal to the length AQ. Then PR will be the tangent to parabola at the point P, and PS drawn perpendicular to PR will be the normal to the curve at the same point.

Hyperbola

A hyperbola with asymptotes OX and OY is shown in Fig. 4·33, and it is required to draw a tangent to the curve at any point such as P which lies on the curve. Draw PQ parallel to OX to cut OY at Q. Mark off QR equal in length to OR and join P to R. Then PR is the tangent to the curve at the point P, and PS perpendicular to PR is the normal to the hyperbola at the same point.

It should be noted that the tangent may be obtained by drawing the line PM parallel to the other asymptote OY and marking off MN equal to MO, and either construction may also be used for a rectangular hyperbola or the alternative curves where the asymptote is inclined at an obtuse angle.

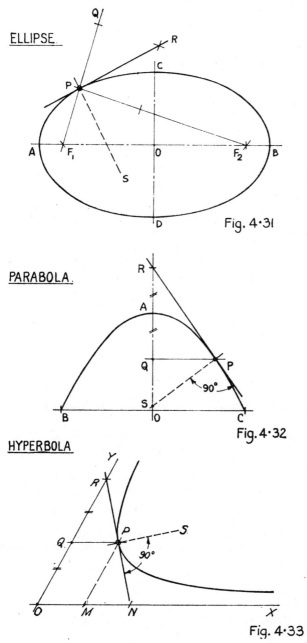

ELLIPSE.

Fig. 4·31

PARABOLA.

90°

Fig. 4·32

HYPERBOLA

90°

Fig. 4·33

146

GEOMETRICAL CONSTRUCTIONS

Problem Assignments

1. Draw, FULL SIZE, the pawl illustrated in Fig. 4·34, clearly showing all essential construction.

2. Draw, FULL SIZE, the valve rocker arm illustrated in Fig. 4·35. All construction lines must be shown.

3. Draw, FULL SIZE, the machine cam illustrated in Fig. 4·36. All important construction must be clearly shown.

4. Draw, FULL SIZE, the profile illustrated in Fig. 4·37. The method of construction must be clearly indicated.

5. Draw, FULL SIZE, a true ellipse using the rectangular method of construction. The major and minor axes are respectively 150 mm and 90 mm long. Show necessary construction.

6. Draw, FULL SIZE, a true ellipse using the auxiliary circles method. The lengths of the major and minor axes are respectively 140 mm and 70 mm. Essential construction must be shown. Draw the tangent and normal to the curve at any point P lying on the curve.

7. With the aid of a compass draw, FULL SIZE, an approximate ellipse having a major axis of 130 mm and a minor axis of 75 mm. All construction must be shown.

8. The foci of an ellipse are 100 mm apart and a point on the surve is 40 mm from both the major and minor axes. Draw the ellipse FULL SIZE, and show all important construction. Measure and state the length of the two axes.

9. Draw a parallelogram ABCD so that the base AB=150 mm, BC=120 mm, and the angle BAD=60°.
Mark off along CD a point P so that DP=12 mm. Let AD and AB represent the asymptotes of a hyperbola and let P be a given point on the curve.
Construct that part of the hyperbola which lies within the parallelogram. Draw the tangent and normal to the curve at any point Q which lies on the curve.

10. Draw a rectangle 200 mm high and 135 mm long.
Construct the parabola which would be just contained by the rectangle. Select any point P on the curve (not at the vertex) and through P draw the tangent and normal to the curve.

11. Draw a right-angled triangle ABC. AC (the vertical side)= 200 mm, AB (Base)=75 mm.
Construct a parabola which will pass through B so that BC is tangential to the curve at B. Let the axis of the curve lie along AC and let the base of the parabola contain the line AB.

147

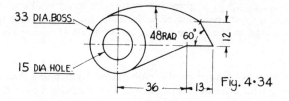

Fig. 4·34

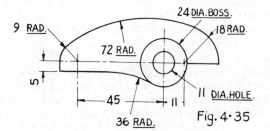

Fig. 4·35

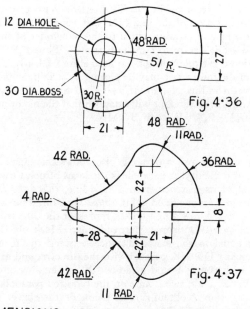

Fig. 4·36

Fig. 4·37

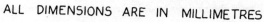

ALL DIMENSIONS ARE IN MILLIMETRES

148

LOCI

The second group of engineering curves are more readily understood, perhaps, if they are regarded as problems in loci, and as an introduction to this conception the conics will be re-examined as typical examples.

Definition

A locus may be defined as the path traced by a point that moves in accordance with a stated law of motion. For instance, a *straight line* may be defined as the path traced by a point that moves so that at any instant the ratio of its perpendicular distances from two fixed points is a constant. A *circle* may be similarly defined as the path of a point that moves but remains at a constant distance from a given fixed point.

Ellipse

An ellipse may be defined as the path traced by a point that moves so that at any instant the sum of its distances from two fixed points is a constant. The two fixed points are termed the foci of the ellipse and in Fig. 5·1 the foci F_1 and F_2 have been marked out at a given distance apart on a line that will contain the major axis. The constant for the ellipse is given by the length MN, shown beneath Fig. 5·1. From this information a series of points on the curve may be readily plotted. With centre F_1 and a radius equal to a portion of the line MN—say length ML—draw an arc, and with centre F_2 and a radius equal to the remainder of the line—i.e. LN—a second arc is drawn to cut the first at P. Thus $F_1P + F_2P = MN$ and by definition P is a point on the required ellipse. Clearly, the extremities C and D of the minor axis may be plotted by striking equal arcs from F_1 and F_2 with a radius of *half MN*—i.e. so that $F_1C + F_2C = MN = F_1D + F_2D$. And a little thought will establish that the major axis is equal to MN since $F_1A + F_2A = F_1B + F_2B = MN$.

Parabola

The following definition of a parabola also allows this curve to be constructed without difficulty. A parabola is the locus of point that moves so that at any instant its distance from a fixed line, *called the Directrix*, is equal to its distance from a fixed point, *called the focus*. The construction is shown in Fig. 5·2. Draw a line DD to represent the directrix and from any convenient point O drop a perpendicular. Mark off OF on this perpendicular equal to the stated distance between the focus and the directrix. Draw any line KK parallel with the directrix and at a distance "X" from it; with centre F and a radius "X" strike arcs to cut KK at points P and P_1 to obtain two points on the required parabola.

Repeat construction to obtain further points on the curve. The vertex A of the parabola will be at the mid-point of OF and must lie on the axis of the curve.

ELLIPSE.

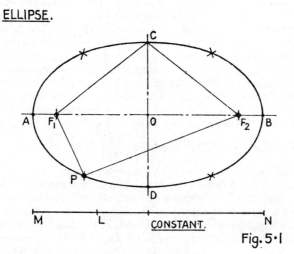

Fig. 5·1

PARABOLA.

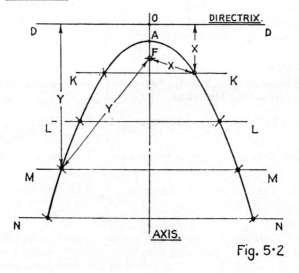

Fig. 5·2

LOCI

Hyperbola

A hyperbola may be defined as the locus of a point that moves so that the ratio between its distances from a fixed point and a fixed line is a constant, the fixed point being the focus of the curve and the fixed line the directrix. The ratio between these two distances is termed the *Eccentricity of the Conic*, and for a hyperbola the ratio has a value always greater than unity.

In the present example an eccentricity of 1·125 has been assumed and to enable this ratio to be maintained graphically it is usual to construct a proportional scale as shown in Fig. 5·3. In this diagram two lines OA and OB are drawn with an inclination of any convenient angle. Along OA mark off a length OM equal to 4 units, and along OB mark off a length OM, equal to $4\frac{1}{2}$ units. Then the ratio $\dfrac{OM_1}{OM} = \frac{9}{8} = 1·125$.

The construction of the hyperbola is shown in Fig. 5·4—draw the line DD to represent the directrix and at a point O draw the axis of the curve perpendicular to DD. On this axis mark off OF equal to the distance between the focus F and the directrix. Draw any line KK parallel with the directrix and transfer the axial distance of this line from the directrix to the line OA of the proportional scale, Fig. 5·3—i.e. the distance OK. From K draw a line parallel with MM_1 to cut OB at K_1—then OK_1 is the corresponding focal distance. With centre F and a radius OK_1, strike arcs above and below the axis in Fig. 5·4 to cut the line KK as shown. K_2 and K_3 are points on the required hyperbola. Further points on the curve may be determined in a similar manner.

Eccentricity

Fig. 5·5 indicates the relationship between the three conics, the Ellipse, the Parabola and the Hyperbola.

(a) *The eccentricity of an ellipse* $\dfrac{FP}{PD}$ *is always* < Unity.

(b) *The eccentricity of a parabola* $\dfrac{FP_1}{P_1D_1}$ *is always* = 1.

(c) *The eccentricity of a hyperbola* $\dfrac{FP_2}{P_2D_2}$ *is always* > Unity.

Tangents

It is often necessary to construct the tangent to a conic, and of the many different methods the following is probably the most useful because it may be used for all three conics providing the focus and directrix are known. Fig. 5·6 illustrates this common construction. Let P be the point of contact of the required tangent. Join P to the focus F and from F draw a line perpendicular to FP to cut the directrix at Q .Then Q is another point on the tangent, and the line PQ is the tangent required.

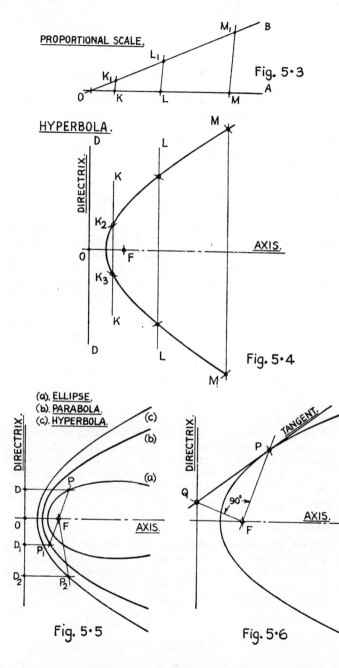

PROPORTIONAL SCALE.

Fig. 5·3

HYPERBOLA.

AXIS.

Fig. 5·4

(a). ELLIPSE.
(b). PARABOLA.
(c). HYPERBOLA.

DIRECTRIX.

AXIS.

Fig. 5·5

DIRECTRIX.

TANGENT.

90°

AXIS.

Fig. 5·6

LOCI

Cycloidal Curves

The cycloidal group of curves are generated by the rolling action of a circle or disc which moves along a straight or curved path without slip, and they are of special interest because they give the tooth profile that is used in the cycloidal system of gearing. The simplest of these curves is the *Cycloid* for which the circle rolls in one plane along a straight line, and by plotting the locus of a single point on the periphery of a circle the shape of the cycloid may be readily reproduced.

Cycloid

Fig. 5·7 indicates the method of construction. Let AB represent the straight-line path followed by the rolling circle, and at A draw the circle in conctact with the line. While the circle revolves once in a clockwise direction it will move from left to right a distance equal to the circumference of the circle, therefore mark off a distance AB equal to πD.

Note that, although this distance may be calculated and accurately scaled, it is usual to determine the length AB by one of the many graphical methods, the choice being decided by the degree of accuracy required. Divide the circle into any convenient number of equal parts, say 8 or 12, and divide AB into the same number of equal parts. When the circle has made half a revolution, the initial point of contact A will clearly be diametrically opposite—i.e. at the point indicated by A_4. Intermediate points for the whole cycle may be readily determined by drawing the circle in a series of intermediate positions and marking off the corresponding positions reached by the point A.

Epicycloid

Where the circle rolls without slip along the *outside* of a circular path, as shown in Fig. 5·8, the resultant locus of any point on the circle is called an *Epicycloid*. The method of constructing this curve is clearly indicated in Fig. 5·8, but, as shown in the previous example, it merely involves drawing the circle or disc in successive positions and to mark for each the point reached by A, the initial point of contact.

Hypocycloid

A *Hypocycloid* is the locus of a point on the periphery of a circle that rolls without slip on the *inside* of a circular path, as shown in Fig. 5·9. The diagram is no doubt self-explanatory, but it should be noted that in this case the disc must rotate in an anti-clockwise direction in order to move along the inside of the curve from A to B.

CYCLOID.

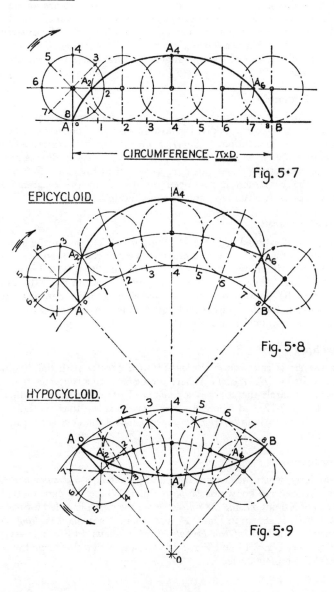

CIRCUMFERENCE _ πxD.

Fig. 5·7

EPICYCLOID.

Fig. 5·8

HYPOCYCLOID.

Fig. 5·9

154

LOCI

Trochoids

The group of engineering curves known as the *Trochoids* are similar to the cycloidal curves in that they are generated by the action of a circle or disc that rolls without slip along a straight or curved path. The difference is due to the fact that the locus plotted is of a point that lies inside or outside the circle, i.e. of a point attached to the circle but not on the circumference.

Superior Trochoid

The procedure for plotting this curve is exactly the same as that used for the cycloid, i.e. the circle or disc is drawn in a series of positions throughout one cycle or revolution. A *Superior Trochoid* is the path traced by a point *outside* the circle and therefore a crank of suitable radius is reproduced for each intermediate position, as shown in Fig. 5·10. For clarity some of the construction has been omitted from the diagram, but sufficient has been given to enable the method to be understood.

Inferior Trochoid

This curve is illustrated in Fig. 5·11. The *Inferior Trochoid* is the locus of a point inside the circle, i.e. of a crank of smaller radius than the circle, and the only difference in construction is due to this difference in radius. A limited amount of the construction is shown in Fig. 5·11, but it should now be appreciated that an accurate solution depends upon reproducing the rolling circle and the "crank" in each of, a series of intermediate positions throughout the whole cycle.

Epitrochoid

When the circle rolls round the *outside of a circular* path the resultant curve is called an *Epitrochoid*. Where the crank radius is greater than the radius of the circle the curve is a *Superior Epitrochoid*, half of which is shown in Fig. 5·12, and where the crank radius is less than the radius of the circle the curve is an *Inferior Epitrochoid*, half of this curve being shown in Fig. 5·13.

Hypotrochoid

And similarly, when the circle rolls round the *inside of a circular path* the curves obtained are known as *Hypotrochoids*. Where the path plotted is the locus of a point *outside the rolling circle*, the curve is called a *Superior Hypotrochoid*, as shown in Fig. 5·14, and where it is *inside the rolling circle* the curve is called an *Inferior Hypotrochoid*, as shown in Fig. 5·15—these two diagrams, Fig. 5·14 and Fig. 5·15, actually giving the curve for only half of the complete cycle.

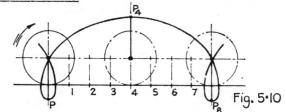

SUPERIOR TROCHOID.

P₄

P   1 2 3 4 5 6 7   P₈ Fig. 5·10

INFERIOR TROCHOID.

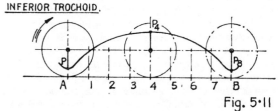

P₄

P   A   1 2 3 4 5 6 7   B   P₈

Fig. 5·11

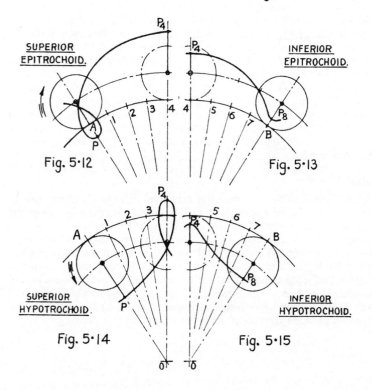

SUPERIOR
EPITROCHOID.

P₄

INFERIOR
EPITROCHOID.

P₄

A   1 2 3 4   4 5 6 7   P₈

P   B

Fig. 5·12   Fig. 5·13

P₄

2 3   5 6 7

A   1   P₄   B

SUPERIOR
HYPOTROCHOID.   P₈

INFERIOR
HYPOTROCHOID.

P'

Fig. 5·14   Fig. 5·15

O   O

156

LOCI

Involute

Gearing with cycloidal tooth profiles will, in general, only be found in watches, clocks and certain fine instruments. For practical reasons the tooth form used for all modern power transmissions is *Involute*, a profile which also gives a constant angular velocity ratio. This curve may be defined as the locus traced by a point on a straight line or rod which rolls without slip round the circumference of a circle, but is perhaps more readily understood by regarding it as the path followed by a point on a cord or string which is held taut and at the same time unwound from the surface of a cylinder. The method of constructing an involute is illustrated in Fig. 5·16. Draw a circle of any suitable radius and divide its circumference into any number of equal parts—the suggested minimum is twelve divisions, as in the given diagram. From a point A draw a tangent and mark off a length AB equal to half the circumference of the circle—an approximate graphical method being generally satisfactory. Divide the tangent AB into six equal parts, numbered as shown. From the points of division on the circle, numbered 1, 2, 3, 4 and 5, draw tangents and mark off lengths $1P_1$: $2P_2$:$3P_3$: $4P_4$ and $5P_5$ respectively equal to 1, 2, 3, 4 and 5 divisions of AB. The curve drawn through the points P: P_1: P_2: P_3: P_4: P_5 and P_6 is an *Involute*. It will be understood that the above is the involute for half the circumference, and where the complete involute is required tangents from the unnumbered divisions on the circle must be drawn and the appropriate portions of the whole circumference marked off accordingly.

Spiral

The Archimedean Spiral is the curve generated by a line that rotates about one of its ends while a point moves continuously along the line, both the angular and linear motions being uniform. The construction of this curve is shown in Fig. 5·17, where a line AB rotates about end B while a point P moves from B towards A. Radial lines are drawn from B at intervals of 30 degrees and, as the linear motion is also uniform, the units of length set off along these radial lines are in arithmetic progression, i.e. BP has a length of 1 unit, BP_2 a length of 2 units, BP_3 a length of 3 units, and so on depending upon the length of spiral required. In the diagram, nine angular and linear increments have been plotted.

INVOLUTE.

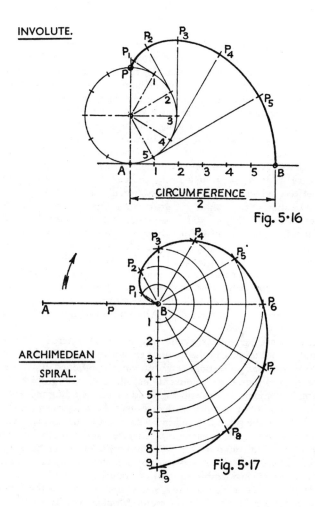

CIRCUMFERENCE
2

Fig. 5·16

ARCHIMEDEAN

SPIRAL.

Fig. 5·17

158

LOCI

Helix

Another curve of special interest to engineers is the *Helix*, since screw threads and coiled springs are helical in form. The curve may be defined as the locus of a point that moves on the surface of a cylinder so that the ratio between its angular and its linear motion is a constant. Thus, the groove that is cut or rolled into the surface of a cylinder to produce a screw thread advances axially the same amount for each revolution—the axial movement per revolution being known as the *Pitch* of the thread. In the case of a *tension spring*, wire is *close-wound* on the surface of a cylindrical bar so that each "turn" of wire touches the adjacent turns and clearly the axial movement per revolution is then equal to the diameter of the wire. With a *compression spring* the coils are *open-wound* and the space between adjacent turns of wire is normally constant.

Fig. 5·18 shows the method of construction. Draw a circle of diameter D to represent the circular rod or cylinder and, in projection with the centre of this circle, set off a line AB to represent to the same scale the axial movement per revolution—i.e. the pitch of the helix. Complete the rectangle of length AB and height D, divide AB into twelve equal parts and erect ordinates at these division points. Divide the circle into twelve equal sectors, numbering them as shown in the diagram. Project from the points 0, 1, 2, 3, etc., on the circle to intersect the corresponding ordinates from the points 0, 1, 2, 3, etc., along AB. The curve joining these points of intersection is a *Helix*.

While there are many cases, particularly in design, where it is necessary to accurately plot a helix in the manner shown above, it should be noted that in the simple applications such as those mentioned it is usual to compromise and reproduce a conventional illustration. Fig. 5·19 shows a short length of square thread and Fig. 5·20 a corresponding piece of Vee-form thread; in both examples the helices have been replaced by straight lines and, where the pitch is small in relation to the thread diameter, the resulting picture is quite satisfactory. A tension and compression spring are respectively illustrated in Figs. 5·21 and 5·22, and it can be seen that again the helices have been replaced by straight lines. This practice obviously saves a considerable amount of draughting time.

The Helix may be recognized as a Sine Curve and also as the displacement curve for a point that has Harmonic Motion (S.H.M.).

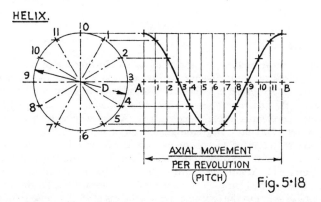

HELIX.

0
1
2
3
4
5
6
7
8
9
10
11
D
A
B
AXIAL MOVEMENT
PER REVOLUTION
(PITCH)

Fig. 5·18

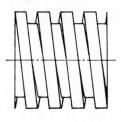

SQUARE THREAD.

Fig. 5·19

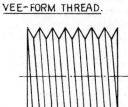

VEE-FORM THREAD.

Fig. 5·20

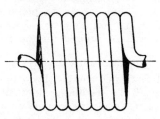

TENSION SPRING

Fig. 5·21

COMPRESSION SPRING.

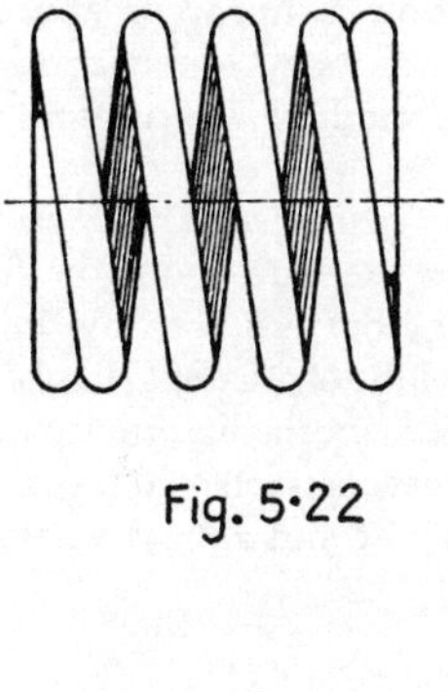

Fig. 5·22

LOCI

Mechanisms

One of the most useful applications of loci is plotting the paths traced by "Key" points on a moving mechanism so that suitable guards may be designed. Every projecting feature of a machine is a potential source of danger to the machine operator, and it is a prime necessity to provide adequate safeguards where danger exists. A typical case is shown in Fig. 5·23, which illustrates diagrammatically an engine or pump mechanism. The line of action of the piston or ram is off-set from the axis of the crankshaft, and the extreme positions of the connecting rod AB are then unsymmetrical. A suitable guard could have the form indicated by the dotted line. In this simple case it was only necessary to plot the extreme positions of AB, but the example is nevertheless useful because it indicates the general procedure, i.e. that the loci of points such as A and B are plotted *for a series of different positions of the mechanism within its complete cycle of operations*.

The mechanism shown in Fig. 5·24 requires more detailed treatment. The crank AO_1 rotates continuously about its centre O_1 and at A is connected by a pin joint to a connecting rod BC. A trunnion bearing at O_2 provides a sliding connection for the rod BC so that whatever its angular position the line of action of BC will always pass through the point O_2. It is required to plot the locus of the points B and C, and the crank-pin A is therefore drawn in twelve or more different positions, such as A_1, and for each of them the corresponding positions of B and C are plotted. Curves drawn through the two sets of points will give the loci shown in the diagram.

Sometimes auxiliary machines or switchgear have to be automatically operated by the parent machine and it becomes necessary to examine the movements of each link, or part, of the main machine to discover a point whose motion is linear or approximately straight. It can be seen that during part of its cycle the locus of C in Fig. 5·24 is almost a straight line and this period of its motion may well be utilized for the purpose suggested.

A similar example is shown in Fig. 5·25, where two links AO_1 and BO_2 respectively oscillate about the fixed centres O_1 and O_2. These links are joined to the bar AB with pin joints, and C is the mid-point of AB. The "figure of eight" locus of C has been plotted while the links move between their limits in both directions, i.e. between A_M and A_N and between B_M and B_N. It can be seen that a considerable portion of the locus is approximately straight and almost vertical.

161

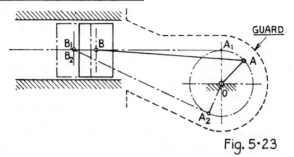

Fig. 5·23

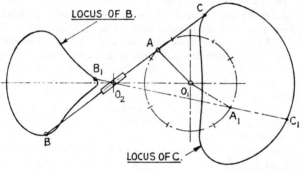

Fig. 5·24

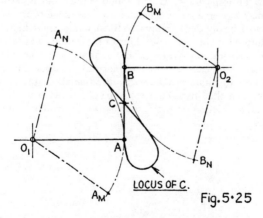

LOCUS OF C.

Fig. 5·25

LOCI

Cams

Linear or angular motion is often imparted to a machine part by a cam which may be defined as a rotating member or link designed for this purpose. And the profile of a cam may be regarded as a locus, since it determines the movement that will be communicated to the machine part—i.e. the follower. In general the motion transmitted has either uniform velocity or S.H.M. Fig. 5·26 shows the method of plotting the profile of a cam that will impart a vertical, straight-line motion to a follower, raising and lowering the follower with uniform velocity during each revolution of the cam. It is assumed that the cam has a uniform angular velocity. The follower has to move along the line AB between the limits 0 and 6, and as its velocity must be uniform this distance is divided into six equal parts, to give six upward increments and six downward increments for a full cycle. The equal divisions in the linear movement of the follower must correspond to equal angular divisions in the movement of the cam and thus the circle drawn about the centre of rotation of the cam must be divided into twelve 30° divisions, as shown in the diagram. The remainder of the construction is self-evident and it will be seen that the two halves of this "heart-shaped" cam profile are, in fact, spiral curves. Fig. 5·27 emphasizes the fact that, in this instance, there is "point contact" between the cam and its follower.

The construction required to find the cam profile that will transmit S.H.M. to the follower is shown in Fig. 5·28. The line of stroke of the follower is again vertical, and it also passed through the centre of rotation of the cam. To impart S.H.M. the follower must move harmonically for equal angular movements of the cam, and the range of movement 0 to 6 must therefore be divided as shown in the diagram, these increments being radially plotted on the corresponding cam position. These diagrams are really polar displacement diagrams and to appreciate what takes place it is useful to regard the cam as held stationary and to cause the line of action of the follower to rotate *in the reverse direction* about the cam. It should be noted that in this instance a roller has been fitted to the follower in order to reduce friction—i.e. the mechanism has roller contact as shown in Fig. 5·29.

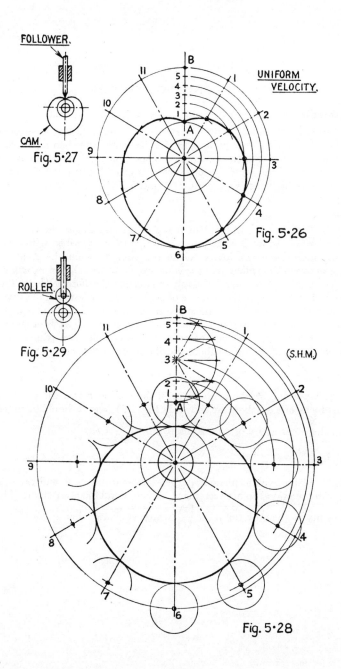

FOLLOWER.

CAM.

Fig. 5·27

UNIFORM
VELOCITY.

B

11
10
9
8
7
6
5

1
2
3
4

A

Fig. 5·26

ROLLER.

Fig. 5·29

(S.H.M.)

B

11
10
9
8
7
6
5

1
2
3
4

A

Fig. 5·28

164

APPENDIX ON CONIC SECTIONS

Introduction

The ellipse, parabola and hyperbola have been discussed first as sections produced by cutting through a right circular cone, and then as the loci of points moving under constrained conditions. A more complete understanding of these very special curves is given by an examination of the following diagrams (Figs. 5·30, 5·31 and 5·32).

Ellipse

In Fig. 5·30 XX is the cutting plane that produces the ellipse shown in the projected view Section XX. Suppose a sphere to be inscribed within the cone to touch the section plane XX at the point F_1 while the points of contact between the sphere and the cone are T_1 and T_2. Then F_1 will be one focus of the ellipse—and the sphere is called the *Focal Sphere*. The sphere and cone have, in fact, a circle of contact and the length T_1T_2 is the diameter of this circle. If the plane of this circle is produced to meet the section plane at D, the position of the directrix of the ellipse is obtained. The directrix is thus the line of contact between the two planes—the plane of contact of the focal sphere and the plane of the section XX.

Parabola

The corresponding relationship between the section plane, the directrix and the focus of a parabola are shown in Fig. 5·31, and it should be noted that as the eccentricity of a parabola is unity $\dfrac{FA}{AO} = 1$.

Hyperbola

In Fig. 5·32 the section plane is perpendicular to the base and the corresponding relationship between plane, directrix and focus are shown. The eccentricity is given by the ratio $\dfrac{FA}{AO}$ which is greater than unity.

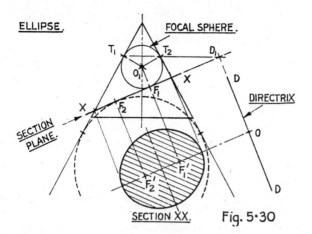

ELLIPSE.

FOCAL SPHERE.

T_1 T_2 O_1 D_1 D

F_1 X DIRECTRIX

SECTION PLANE. X F_2 O

F_1' F_2' D

SECTION XX. Fig. 5·30

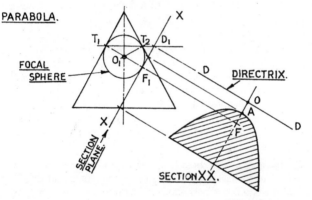

PARABOLA.

X

T_1 T_2 D_1 O_1 D DIRECTRIX.

FOCAL SPHERE F_1 O A D

X F

SECTION PLANE. SECTION XX.

Fig. 5·31

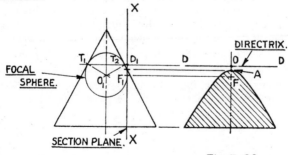

HYPERBOLA.

X

DIRECTRIX.

FOCAL SPHERE. T_1 T_2 D_1 D O D

O_1 F_1 A F

SECTION PLANE. X

Fig. 5·32

LOCI

Problem Assignments

1. The focus of a parabola is 20 mm from its directrix. Plot the curve FULL SIZE, showing all essential construction, and then draw a tangent through a point on the curve that is 45 mm from the axis of the parabola. Axial length of curve = 75 mm.

2. A disc of 50 mm diameter rolls without slip round the outside of another disc of 150 mm diameter. Plot, FULL SIZE, the path traced by a point on the circumference of the 50 mm disc while it makes one complete revolution. The large disc remains stationary.

3. A wheel of 38 mm diameter rolls without slip round the outside of a fixed wheel of 110 mm diameter. A crank of 50 mm radius is rigidly attached to the rotating wheel. Plot, FULL SIZE, the path traced by the crank pin for one complete cycle.

4. Plot, FULL SIZE and for one complete revolution, the locus of a point in a disc which rolls without slip round the inside of a circular path of 100 mm radius. The rotating disc is 50 mm diameter and the point 20 mm from the centre of the disc.

5. An Archimedean Spiral is generated by a point that moves uniformly along a line while the line rotates about one end. The line is 75 mm long and the point moves towards the centre of rotation and traverses the whole length of the line while the latter makes two complete revolutions. Plot the curve FULL SIZE, showing all essential construction.

6. Draw, FULL SIZE, the involute of a circle of 50 mm diameter. The length of curve required is that generated by half the circumference of the circle.

7. The focus of a hyperbola is 28 mm from its directrix and the eccentricity of the curve is 1·25. Plot the curve FULL SIZE and draw a tangent through a point on the hyperbola that is 62 mm from the directrix. Assume that the curve has a maximum axial length of 100 mm.

8. The line ABC in Fig. 5·33 shows the cross-section of a sheet-steel chute that is wrapped round and welded to a central column of 375 mm diameter. The chute is helical in form and has a pitch of 900 mm. Draw one complete turn of the chute using a scale 1/10 FULL SIZE.

9. A slider crank mechanism is illustrated in Fig. 5·34. Draw the mechanism FULL SIZE and plot the locus of the point C.

10. Draw, FULL SIZE, the mechanism illustrated in Fig. 5·35 and plot the path traced by the point C for a complete cycle.

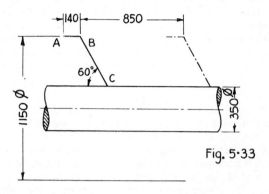

Fig. 5·33

ALL DIMENSIONS ARE
IN MILLIMETRES

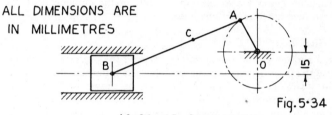

Fig. 5·34

AO = 24 : AB = 96 : AC = 36

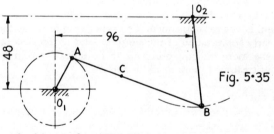

Fig. 5·35

AO₁ = 24 : AB = 96 : BO₂ = 60 : AC = 36

168

INTERSECTIONS

Definition

An intersection is merely the "edge" or line of junction between any two adjoining surfaces of an object and, providing one of the surfaces is visible the intersection line will also be visible and, in consequence, will be illustrated by a continuous line. To emphasize this, it may be said that most of the outlines drawn to represent any solid object are theoretically intersection lines—and this is true for both pictorial and orthographic projections.

Plane Surfaces

In many cases the adjoining faces are flat—i.e. *plane surfaces*—and the resultant line of intersection is a *straight line*. This has been demonstrated in all the preceding examples, but to ensure that this is clearly understood Figs. 6·1 and 6·2 should be carefully examined and compared. The junction between the surfaces A and B has been heavily lined in the isometric view, Fig. 6·1 and the corresponding faces in the orthographic views have been marked with the same letters of the alphabet. All the lines in both diagrams are straight lines.

Inclined Surfaces

In Figs. 6·3 and 6·4 two of the boundary faces of the object are *inclined*, but because the faces are again plane surfaces, the intersection of them is once again a straight line. And this line can be drawn with the same facility as the intersections in Figs. 6·1 and 6·2 because the position of both ends of the line can be directly projected as indicated in Fig. 6·4.

It should be noted that because the junction between two plane surfaces (*a*) is a straight line and (*b*) can be obtained by direct projection, it is seldom regarded as an intersection problem. This limitation in conception is not recommended. The experience of the authors suggests that an early appreciation of the simplest kind of intersection eventually enables the more difficult problems to be quickly recognized, and the method of treatment more easily understood.

Curved Surfaces

When curved surfaces are introduced, the resultant intersection is not, as a rule, a straight line—nor can it be projected "on inspection" as in the above examples. Fig. 6·5 illustrates a simple case where only one of the boundary faces is curved—i.e. surface E. It will be assumed that the two elevations are the orthographic views given in Fig. 6·7 and it is required to project the plan. The necessary construction is graphically illustrated in the "exploded" pictorial view shown in Fig. 6·6, the object being regarded as cut by *two parallel section planes* AA and BB. These arbitrarily chosen section planes reproduced in Fig. 6·7 immediately give the length and width of the respective sections, and the projection of these into the plan enables the points *a* and *b* to be obtained.

The points *a* and *b* show where the surface E and F meet in the chosen section planes, and the curve drawn through them to the top and bottom surfaces will enable the plan to be completed.

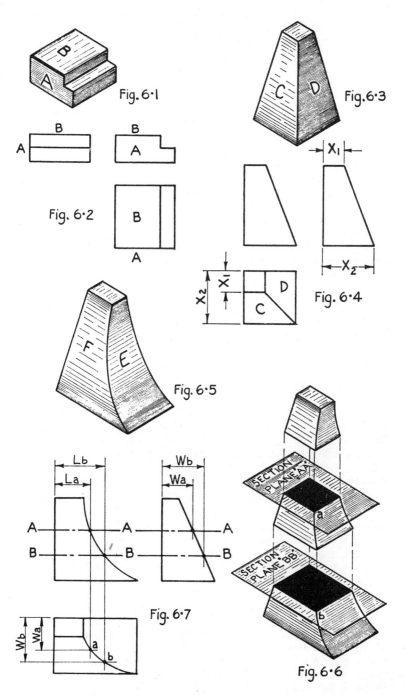

Fig. 6·1

B
A

B
A

Fig. 6·2

B
A

Fig. 6·3

C D

X₁

X₂

X₂ X̄ D
     C

Fig. 6·4

F E

Fig. 6·5

Lb
La

Wb
Wa

A —— A —— A

B —— B —— B

Wb Wa

a b

Fig. 6·7

SECTION PLANE 'A'

a

SECTION PLANE 'BB'

b

Fig. 6·6

INTERSECTIONS

Problems and Solutions

Example 1

Two elevations of a block are given in Fig. 6·8 and it is required to *project the plan.*

The rectangular outline of the plan view, and of the groove, may be obtained by direct projection. To reproduce the intersection between the curved surfaces it is necessary to consider a number of section planes. Draw a horizontal section plane AA across the given views. The position of the plane is arbitrary providing it cuts both curved surfaces. Neglecting the groove, the plane AA produces a surface of length L_a and width W_a which projected into plan determines the two points a_1 and a_2. Another horizontal section plane BB will produce in plan two corresponding points b_1 and b_2 and additional planes may be used when necessary to enable the complete intersection curve to be drawn. A pictorial view of the object is shown in Fig. 6·9.

Example 2

An end view and plan of a short length of moulding are given in Fig. 6·10. The moulding is cut along a curved surface of radius R as shown in the plan. Project the elevation of the moulding.

First project the plane surface to obtain the outline of the elevation and the rectangular surface S. Now draw the *vertical* section plane AA in both the end view and the plan. The point of junction of AA with the curved profile shown in the end view is projected horizontally to the elevation to meet the corresponding point projected vertically from the plan to obtain the point *a* on the intersection. Similar projections for the vertical plane BB will determine the point *b* and enable the curve of intersection to be completed. Fig. 6·11 illustrates the moulding pictorially.

Example 3

This problem is presented in a rather different form. The object shown in Figs. 6·12 and 6·13 is a solid of revolution with a horizontal axis; it may be regarded as turned in a lathe from a large to a small diameter with the transition between the two diameters following a curved profile of radius R_1. From this basic shape a circular groove of radius R_2 is machined as shown in the elevation of Fig. 6·12. The elevation is a complete view, but only the outline is given in the end view. The end view is required to be completed and the plan projected.

Consider the *vertical plane* XX shown in the end view. Clearly this plane will produce a circular section of diameter D_x and when this is drawn in the elevation its termination at the curved surface of radius R_2 is immediately found. The two terminal points returned to the initial section plane XX provide two points on the intersection curve. Repeating the construction for plane YY will determine the position of additional points on the curve.

171

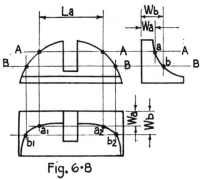

La Wb Wa

A   A   A
B   B   a   B
              b

Wa
Wb

a₁   a₂
b₁   b₂

Fig. 6·8

Fig. 6·9

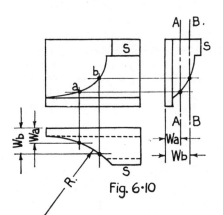

S

A   B

b   S
a

A   B

Wb
Wa

Wa
Wb

R.

S

Fig. 6·10

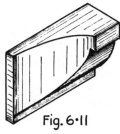

Fig. 6·11

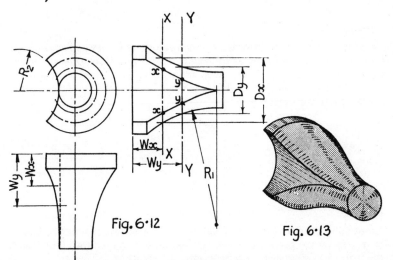

X   Y

R₂

x
y
y
x

Dy
Dx

Wx   X
Wy   Y

Wy
Wx

R₁

Fig. 6·12

Fig. 6·13

172

INTERSECTIONS

Problem Assignments

Exercise 1

A 75mm diameter cylinder is cut as shown in Fig. 6·14. Draw the given view FULL SIZE and project a plan from view A as seen from the direction of arrow B. All essential construction must be shown.

Exercise 2

The object shown in Fig. 6·15 is cylindrical in form and its axis is vertical Material has been machined from the original cylinder along the axis from A to B and then along a plane BC that is inclined at 30 degrees to the axis. Draw the given elevation FULL SIZE and then project an end view as indicated by the arrows. All essential construction must be shown.

Exercise 3

Part of a right circular cone is illustrated at Fig. 6·16, the axis of the cone being horizontal. The cone has been cut by an inclined plane that is parallel with one of the sloping sides. Draw the given view FULL SIZE, project an end view looking in the direction of the arrow A, and beneath the given view project the plan. All essential construction must be shown.

Exercise 4

The object shown in Fig. 6·17 is made from a solid of revolution that has been turned in a lathe. The transition between the two diameters follows a curved path of 120 mm radius. After the turning operation two flat and parallel faces are milled as shown in the end view. Draw the given views FULL SIZE, complete the elevation E and then project a plan. All essential construction must be shown.

Exercise 5

An ornamental cap is illustrated by the orthographic views given in Fig. 6·18. A "vee" groove with a flank angle of 90 degrees has to be cut from the object, as indicated in the plan. Draw, FULL SIZE, an elevation, plan and end view of the cap after the groove has been machined. All essential construction must be shown.

Exercise 6

The plan of a circular chain link, or toroid, that has been cut by a section plane XX is shown in Fig. 6·19. Draw the given view FULL SIZE and then project an elevation as seen from the direction of the arrows. All essential construction must be shown.

Exercise 7

An oblique cylinder (see Fig. 6·20) is cut by a section plane XX. Draw FULL SIZE (*a*) the given end view, (*b*) Section XX, (*c*) beneath (*b*) project the plan. All essential construction must be shown.

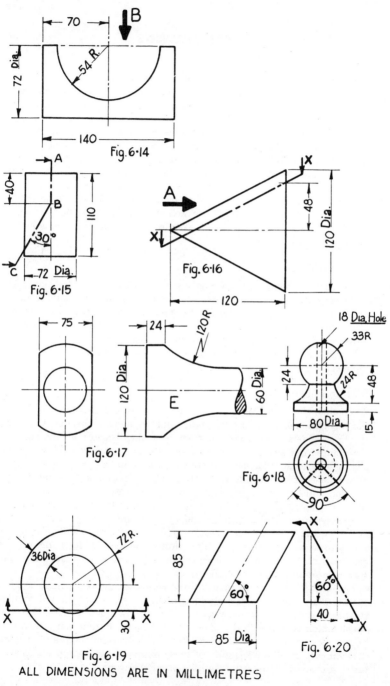

Fig. 6·14

Fig. 6·15

Fig. 6·16

Fig. 6·17

18 Dia. Hole
33R
24R
80 Dia.
Fig. 6·18
90°

Fig. 6·19

Fig. 6·20

ALL DIMENSIONS ARE IN MILLIMETRES

174

PENETRATIONS

Definition

When two solids intersect, i.e. one penetrates another as in Fig. 6·21, the edge or junction between the meeting surfaces is called a penetration curve. Fig. 6·21 illustrates the penetration of a small cylinder into another of larger diameter. In Fig. 6·22 the small cylinder is shown withdrawn from the larger one to reveal the circular hole which would, of course, be just able to receive the penetrating cylinder. There can be little doubt that the edge of junction between the two cylinders in Fig. 6·21 will have exactly the same shape as the edge of junction between the large cylinder and the penetrating hole in Fig. 6·22. It follows that there is *no practical difference* between the two problems—*and there is no difference in the method of treatment*. It is merely a matter of convenience to consider how to project the edges of a single object before examining those cases that involve two or more objects.

Plane Surfaces

In the case of a single object we have seen that the junction between plane surfaces is always a straight line. The result is exactly the same when we are concerned with the junction between a number of objects—if the adjoining surfaces are plane then the intersections or penetrations may be reproduced by direct projection. This is clearly demonstrated in Figs. 6·23 and 6·24 where the objects illustrated are square prisms whose axes intersect at right angles.

Inclined Surfaces

The solids shown in Fig. 6·25 are again square prisms, but in this case the axis of one is inclined to the horizontal. In spite of this new condition the lines of penetration are again straight lines because all the surfaces are plane—and again no special construction is required. However, in Fig. 6·26 a rectangular prism is shown penetrating a hexagonal pyramid; all the faces of both solids are again plane surfaces and the intersections are consequently straight lines, but in this case the lines cannot be directly projected. This is due to the variation in the cross-sectional area of the pyramid. This area has a maximum value at the base and is zero at the apex and, because of this, the penetration points *a* and *b* cannot be reproduced on "inspection". The simple solution is to resort to the construction used for the intersection between curved surfaces—i.e. *treatment by successive parallel sections*.

Actually, it is only necessary in this case to consider two parallel section planes, the plane AA that embraces the upper surface of the rectangular prism and the plane BB that coincides with its lower surface. The essential construction is shown in the plan. The hexagonal outline reproduced for both section planes enables the position of the two points a_1 and b_1 to be determined, and the projection of these points to the appropriate planes in the elevation permits the completion of this view.

ɩ

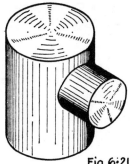

Fig. 6·21

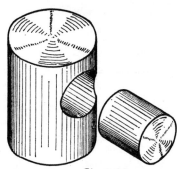

Fig. 6·22

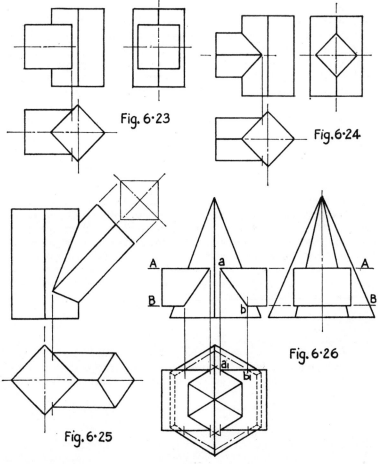

Fig. 6·23

Fig. 6·24

Fig. 6·25

Fig. 6·26

176

PENETRATION OF CURVED SURFACES

Horizontal Planes

Fig. 6·27 shows the plan and part elevation of two cylinders and it is required to complete the elevation by plotting the penetration curve. It is first necessary to project an end view of the small penetrating cylinder, and in this case it is convenient to place this on the right-hand side of the elevation—note that for the purpose of the construction it is unnecessary to draw the complete end view. Consider the horizontal section plane AA which cuts the large cylinder to expose a circular area, as shown in the plan. A little thought will establish that the same plane will cut a rectangular section through the smaller cylinder (see Fig. 6·28) and the partial end view at once determines the width W_a of this rectangle. The projection of this width into the plan enables the point of junction between the two cylinders—*in this plane*—to be found. This point a, is then returned to the initial plane of section in the elevation to find the point a on the penetration curve. Additional horizontal section planes such as BB will enable the complete curve to be drawn. To emphasize the method of treatment the two surfaces exposed by the section plane BB have been cross-hatched in plan—as a rule this is not required.

Vertical Planes 1

The same problem is now examined using vertical planes of section and the construction for this treatment is shown in Fig. 6·29. It will be apparent that a vertical plane such as that indicated in the given plan by the line AA will produce rectangular sections for both cylinders (see Fig. 6·30). Furthermore, the width of the section that is cut through the large cylinder becomes known as soon as the line AA is drawn and it may, therefore, be projected into the elevation without further construction. To determine the corresponding rectangular width cut from the small cylinder, it is only necessary to transfer the section plane to the partial end view that has been reproduced, as before, on the R.H. side of the elevation. The projection of this width into the elevation will establish the points a on the penetration curve, and additional vertical planes will determine the position of further points as required.

Vertical Plane 2

The whole construction is repeated in Fig. 6·31 using the parallel and vertical section plane indicated by the lines AA and BB in this diagram— i.e. planes perpendicular to those used in the preceding treatment. It will be seen that the resultant penetration curve is identical with those obtained in Figs. 6·27 and 6·29.

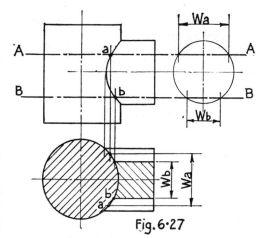

Fig. 6·27

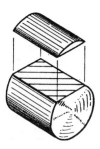

Fig. 6·28

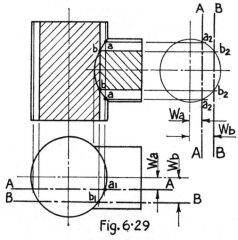

Fig. 6·29

Fig. 6·30

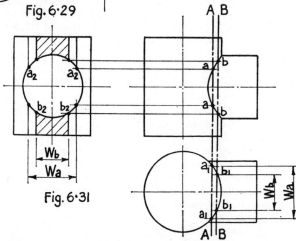

Fig. 6·31

178

PENETRATIONS

Problems and Solutions

Example 1

A cylinder penetrates another of larger diameter, the axes being inclined as shown in Fig. 6·32. Plot the curve of penetration.

The *vertical section planes AA and BB* have been chosen for this problem and a partial end view of the small cylinder is first drawn to enable the width of the two sections to be established. These section planes will expose rectangular surfaces for both cylinders. The essential construction has been shown in the diagram and the surfaces exposed by the section plane BB have been cross-hatched.

Example 2

In Fig. 6·33 a curved rod is shown intersecting a straight cylinder; the diameters are the same and the axes meet at the point P.

In this example it is convenient to use the *vertical section planes AA and BB*. The section planes will produce surfaces of the same width; one of these surfaces will be rectangular, but the other will be curved. It should be noted that only half the surface widths have been drawn, as indicated by the cross-hatched areas reproduced in the diagram for the section AA. The axes meet at the point P and the points of intersection a_0 and b_0 which correspond with the points a and b will both lie on the line OP. The surfaces blend tangentially along this line so that if the cylinder was extended beyond the surface SP the junction would be quite invisible and the penetration would still extend from Q to P as shown in the diagram.

Example 3

The penetration between a cylinder and a right circular cone is shown in Fig. 6·34. To obtain the pentration curve *horizontal section planes AA and BB* have been used. The partial end view will establish the widths W_a and W_b of the cut surfaces of the cylinder. The corresponding rectangles are reproduced in the plan. As the section planes are parallel with the base of the cone, the surfaces exposed by them must also be circular, but their diameter will clearly vary with their distance from the base of the cone. For the plane AA the radius of the circular section is R_a and a circle of this radius is drawn in plan to intersect with the rectangle of width W_a and determine the intersection point a_1. The elevation of a_1 is a point on the required penetration curve.

In this case a plan of the curve has also been drawn.

It is important to pause at this point *to consider why horizontal planes were used in this example*—and, for that matter, why vertical planes were used in example 6·32 and 6·33. The reason is to provide a simple construction that can be very quickly drawn. Vertical planes could be used to solve example 6·34, but the resultant sections through the cone would be hyperbolas.

179

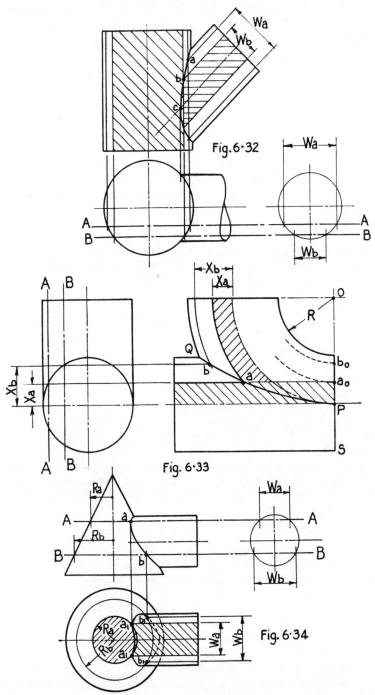

Fig. 6·32

Fig. 6·33

Fig. 6·34

PENETRATIONS

Problem Assignments

Exercise 1

A horizontal trapesoidal prism penetrates an oblique hexagonal pyramid as shown by the orthographic views given in Fig. 6·35. Draw the given views FULL SIZE, complete the left-hand elevation and project a plan as seen from the direction of the arrow A.

Exercise 2

Complete the two given views of the intersecting solids shown at Fig. 6·36 and in addition project an end view looking in the direction of the arrow B. Hidden detail is to be shown in the end view.

Exercise 3

Two cylinders intersect a third cylinder as shown in Fig. 6·37. Draw the given views FULL SIZE, plot the penetration curves and project an end view as seen from the direction of the arrow C.

Exercise 4

A triangular prism penetrates a 75 mm diameter sphere as shown in the views given in Fig. 6·38. Draw the given views FULL SIZE, complete the elevation A and project a plan as seen from the direction of the arrow B.

Exercise 5

An oblique cone is penetrated by an oblique cylinder as shown in Fig. 6·39. Draw the given view FULL SIZE, plot the penetration curve and project a plan and an end view. The projected views must clearly show the curves of penetration.

Exercise 6

An oblique cylinder of 85 mm diameter is intersected by a horizontal irregular prism as shown in Fig. 6·40. Draw the given views FULL SIZE and project a plan as seen from the direction of the arrow C.

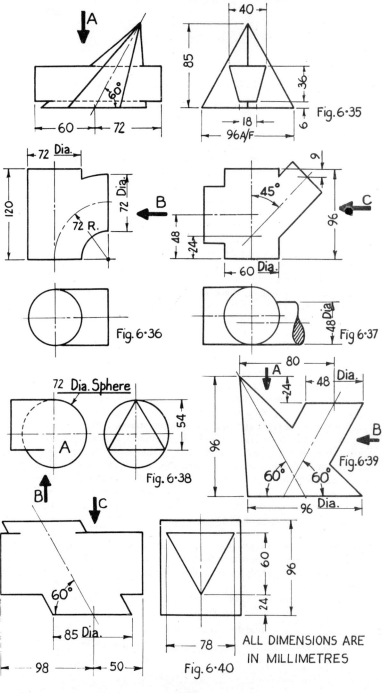

Fig. 6·35

Fig. 6·36

Fig 6·37

72 Dia. Sphere

Fig. 6·38

Fig. 6·39

85 Dia.

ALL DIMENSIONS ARE
IN MILLIMETRES

Fig. 6·40

PENETRATION OF CURVED SURFACES

(Solids of Revolution)

The general method of drawing the line of intersection which is formed when one solid penetrates another is dealt with on page 177. The intersecting solids are cut by a series of section planes, and, by drawing the relevant sectional views, the junction points of the cut surfaces are located. These points lie on the required line of intersection which is drawn through them. *It is emphasized here that this general method, involving the use of section planes, will solve any intersection problem.* When, however, both of the intersecting parts are solids of revolution (i.e. solids in which all sections normal to the axis are circular), a method utilizing *cutting spheres* in place of *cutting planes* often offers an easier solution.

Fig. 6·41 shows a solid of revolution (in this case a right circular cone) which is cut by a sphere, the centre of the sphere being located on the axis of the cone. Two circular edges of intersection are formed where the sphere cuts the cone, and these appear in the plan view as concentric circles, and in the elevation as the straight lines ab and cd. A pictorial view is given at Fig. 6·42. Further thought will show that if any solid of revolution is cut by a sphere whose centre is located on the axis of the solid, the resulting edges of intersection will be circular, and can be projected as circles on a plane perpendicular to the axis of the solid, and as straight lines on any plane which is parallel to the axis of the solid.

This theory is applied to the solution of the problem illustrated at Fig. 6·43 where a right circular cylinder penetrates a right circular cone. The axes of the cone and the cylinder intersect at the point O. If the centre of a cutting sphere is located at O this centre will be located on the axes of *both* solids which will thus be cut in the manner described above. In elevation the lines ab and cd will be produced where the sphere cuts the cone, and the line ef where the sphere cuts the cylinder. The line ef will cut ab at g, and cd at h. The points g and h will lie on the line of intersection of the cone and the cylinder. In plan concentric circles will be produced where the sphere cuts the cone and vertical projectors from the points g and h in elevation will cut these circles to give the position of the junction points in plan, i.e. g_1 and h_1. The solution may now be completed by repeating the process with different sized cutting spheres.

This method offers an easy solution to the fairly wide range of problems which fulfil the following conditions:

(1) Each of the intersecting parts *must be a solid of revolution.*

(2) The axes of the intersecting parts *must intersect.*

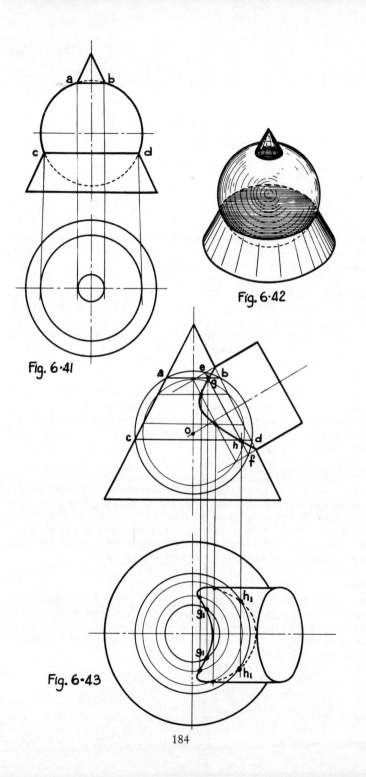

Fig. 6·41

Fig. 6·42

Fig. 6·43

PENETRATIONS

(Solids of Revolution)

Problem Assignments

Exercise 1

A right circular cone is penetrated by the frustum of another right circular cone as illustrated at Fig. 6·44. P is the point at which the axes of the two solids intersect. Draw, FULL SIZE, the given elevation and, vertically beneath it, project a plan. Insert the lines of intersection on both views. All hidden detail must be shown.

Exercise 2

Fig. 6·45 shows the elevation of a paraboloid and a right circular cylinder whose axes intersect at the point P. Draw FULL SIZE the given view and, vertically beneath it, project a plan. Show the edges of intersection on both views and insert all hidden detail.

Exercise 3

Draw FULL SIZE the given elevation of the intersecting right circular cones shown at Fig. 6·46. The axes of the cones intersect at the point P. From this elevation project a plan—the direction of viewing being indicated by the arrow A. Insert the lines of intersection on both views and show all hidden edges.

Exercise 4

A circular hole is drilled through the frustum of a right circular cone as illustrated at Fig. 6·47, the axis of the hole intersecting that of the cone at the point P. Draw the given elevation FULL SIZE and from it project (1) a plan as viewed in the direction of the arrow B and (2) an end view— the direction of viewing being indicated by the arrow C. Show the edges of intersection on all views and insert the hidden detail.

Exercise 5

The axes of the solids of revolution shown at Fig. 6·48 intersect at the point P. Draw, FULL SIZE, the given elevation and from it project (1) a plan as viewed in the direction of the arrow D and (2) an end view as viewed in the direction of the arrow E. Insert the lines of intersection on all views and show all hidden edges.

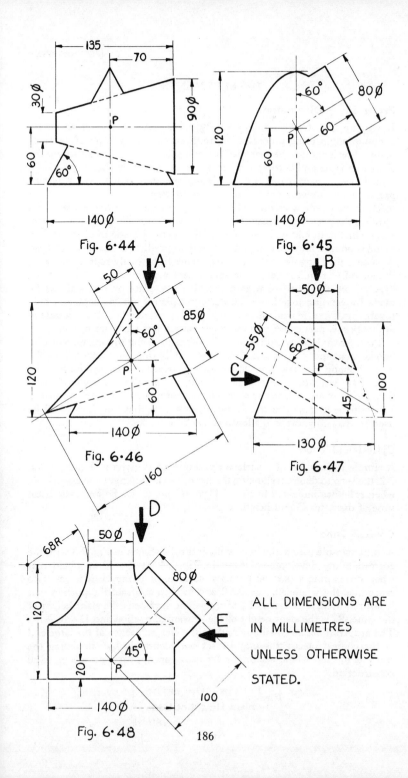

Fig. 6·44

Fig. 6·45

Fig. 6·46

Fig. 6·47

Fig. 6·48

ALL DIMENSIONS ARE
IN MILLIMETRES
UNLESS OTHERWISE
STATED.

186

DEVELOPMENTS

Preliminary Discussion

It will no doubt be useful to briefly review one or two of the more common engineering processes before discussing the subject of developments. For instance, the manufacture of a motor shaft entails turning the shaft in a lathe and cutting away metal from the whole surface of a solid steel bar; in many cases this *machining operation* will follow a *forging process* which roughly produces the desired shape.

To make a hollow engine cylinder a process called *casting* is used; this requires the preliminary manufacture of a wooden replica, called a pattern, from which a mould or impression of the shape is made in sand. Molten metal is poured into the completed mould to produce the cylinder casting. A casting thus enables a complicated shape to be easily reproduced and, in general, it requires very little subsequent machining.

A hollow structure such as a machine bed-plate or pedestal can be made by welding together thick mildsteel plates, cut to shape and held together in a fixture while the *welding process* is carried out. This method of fabrication is particularly useful where only a few parts are needed.

Thin galvanized or tinned sheet is often used for the manufacture of hoods, machine guards, etc. The material is rolled or folded into the desired shape in much the same way as a paper cone is produced. The *flat sheet of metal* that must be initially cut, making allowance where necessary for an overlap in material to effect a joint, is called a *development*.

It will be assumed in the following examples that butt joints will be used so that no additional allowance need be made.

Cylindrical Tube

A simple illustration of a surface development is given in Figs. 7·1 and 7·2, the second diagram showing the flat or plane rectangular shape which, when rolled as indicated in Fig. 7·1, would produce a hollow cylindrical tube of diameter D and height H.

Conical Tube

Another simple case is the hollow conical tube shown in Fig. 7·3 with the corresponding development given in Fig. 7·4. It should be noted that when developing a part of a conical surface, or pyramid, it is easier to reproduce the whole surface OAB and to then subtract the portion that is not required. The radius R_1 of the whole surface is the slant height of the cone, R_2 is the slant height of the unwanted portion and $H = R_1 - R_2$. The arc AB must be equal in length to the circumference of the large end of the conical piece; this may be set out accurately by calculating the angle θ for the whole sector, or by using an approximate geometrical construction.

$$\left(\theta^\circ = \frac{180 \times \text{Base Dia. of Cone}}{\text{Slant Height of Cone}} \right)$$

187

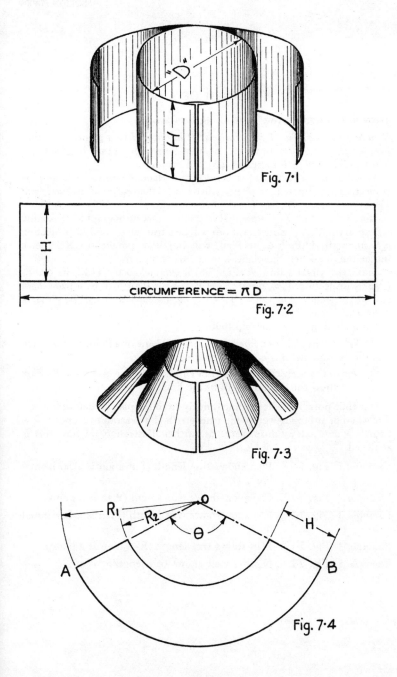

Fig. 7·1

CIRCUMFERENCE = πD

Fig. 7·2

Fig. 7·3

Fig. 7·4

188

TRUE LENGTH OF A LINE (1)

How to Recognize the True Length of a Line

Where a line ab (Fig. 7·5) is *inclined at an angle θ to a plane*, its orthographic projection a_1b_1 upon that plane will be such that the length a_1b_1 is less than ab, and as θ increases a_1b_1 will decrease.

When a line cd (Fig. 7·6) is *parallel* to a plane ($\theta=0$) its orthographic projection c_1d_1 upon that plane will be such that $c_1d_1=cd$ and c_1d_1 *will therefore represent the true length of the line cd.*

If a line, ef (Fig. 7·7) is parallel to the V.P., its orthographic projection e_1f_1 upon the V.P. (i.e. its elevation) will be a true length and its projection e_2f_2 upon the H.P. (i.e. its Plan) will be either parallel to XY (i.e. a horizontal line when the plane is rebatted) or a point.

Similarly, when a line gh (Fig. 7·8) is parallel to the H.P., its orthographic projection, g_1h_1, upon the H.P. (i.e. its Plan) will be a *true length* and its projection g_1h_1 upon the V.P. (i.e. its elevation) will be either a *horizontal line* or a *point.*

Summarizing, it can be said that

(1) Where the *Plan* of a line is a Horizontal Line or a Point its *Elevation* will show the True Length of the line.

(2) When the *Elevation* of a line is a Horizontal Line or a Point its *Plan* will show the True Length of the line.

It is thus possible to determine quickly from the plan and elevation of a line whether either view gives the true length. The examples set out below and their associated figures serve as further illustrations of how this is achieved.

Example 1 (Fig. 7·9). Plan shows true length (Elevation is a horizontal line).

Example 2 (Fig. 7·10). Elevation shows true length (Plan is a point).

Example 3 (Fig. 7·11). Elevation shows true length (Plan is a horizontal line).

Example 4 (Fig. 7·12). Plan shows true length (Elevation is a point).

Example 5 (Fig. 7·13). Neither view shows true length.

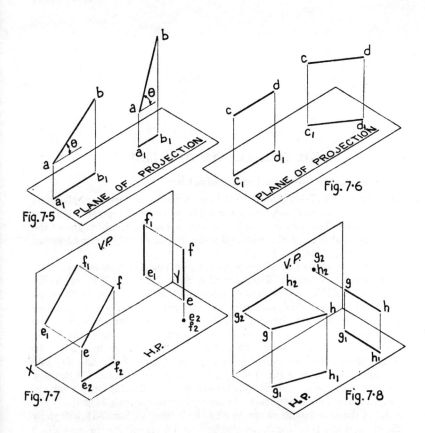

Fig. 7·5

Fig. 7·6

Fig. 7·7

Fig. 7·8

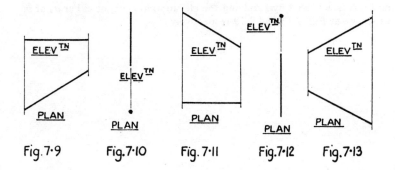

ELEV^{TN}

PLAN

Fig. 7·9

ELEV^{TN}

PLAN

Fig. 7·10

ELEV^{TN}

PLAN

Fig. 7·11

ELEV^{TN}

PLAN

Fig. 7·12

ELEV^{TN}

PLAN

Fig. 7·13

190

THE TRUE LENGTH OF A LINE (2)

How to Obtain the True Length of a Line

If a line ab (Fig. 7·14) is inclined to both vertical and horizontal planes its projections a_vb_v and a_hb_h upon these planes will *not* represent the *true length* of ab. This can be readily seen from Fig. 7·15, which shows the projections of the line ab orthographically (Neither the Plan nor Elevation is a horizontal· line or a point.)

A convenient method of obtaining the true length of ab is shown at Fig. 7·14. The line is rotated about a until it is parallel to the V.P., i.e. to the position ab_1. The projection a_vb_{1v} upon the V.P. is the true length of ab. It should be noted that during the rotating operation the height of b above the H.P. remains unchanged, i.e. $b_1b_{1h}=bb_h$, which means that in the elevation b_v and b_{1v} are in horizontal alignment. To apply this to the orthographic projections of a line, reference should be made to Fig. 7·16 which shows the elevation a_vb_v and the plan a_hb_h of the line ab. The operations for finding the true length of ab are as follows: (1) Revolve a_hb_h about the point a_h until a_hb_{1h} is horizontal in plan; (2) Draw a vertical projector from b_{1h} to intersect a horizontal projector from b_v at b_{1v}. Then a_vb_{1v} is the true length of the line ab. Reference to Fig. 7·17 will show clearly how the true length can also be found by revolving the plan about the point b_h. It is also possible to find the true length in the *plan view* and this is achieved by revolving the elevation a_vb_v about either a_v or b_v as shown at Fig. 7·18 and 7·19 respectively.

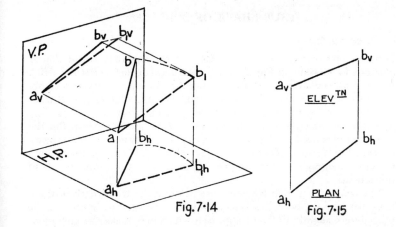

V.P.

H.P.

Fig. 7·14

ELEV^{TN}

PLAN

Fig. 7·15

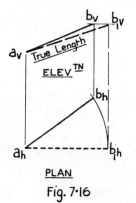

True Length

ELEV^{TN}

PLAN

Fig. 7·16

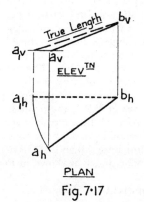

True Length

ELEV^{TN}

PLAN

Fig. 7·17

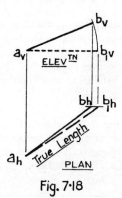

ELEV^{TN}

True Length

PLAN

Fig. 7·18

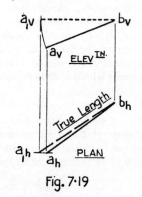

ELEV^{TN.}

True Length

PLAN

Fig. 7·19

192

TRUE SHAPE OF SURFACES

Inclined Surfaces

Consider one of the four sloping faces of the square pyramid that is illustrated pictorially in Fig. 7·20, i.e. *the triangular surface lettered ABC.* Fig. 7·21 immediately reveals that neither the plan nor the elevation shows the true shape of this face. It will be noted, of course, that the plan B_1C_1 of the base edge is a true length because the pyramid is regarded as standing upon a horizontal plane and the elevation of the line is a point. But the two edges produced by the junction between the sloping triangular faces, i.e. *the edges AB and AC in* Fig. 7·20, are clearly not true lengths because in both orthographic views the lines are inclined to the normal planes of projection.

The construction that is widely used to find the true length of these lines has already been described. However, to further emphasize the procedure a slightly different approach which may make the operations easier to visualize is illustrated pictorially in Fig. 7·22. In this diagram the two principal planes of projection V.P.1 and H.P. have been reproduced and, in addition, a second vertical plane V.P.2 has been shown. This additional plane which is perpendicular to the horizontal plane H.P. and inclined at an angle θ to the vertical plane V.P.1 contains one of the inclined lines under consideration, i.e. the line AB in Fig. 7·20 corresponds with the line AB_1 in Fig. 7·22. The normal elevation of the line is illustrated by AB and its plan by the line A_1B_1. Revolving the plane V.P.2 about its edge of contact with the principal vertical plane V.P.1 *until it is in the same plane as* V.P.1, the point B_1 will take up the position of the point B_2 and AB_2 will be the true image of the inclined line. The corresponding orthographic view of the construction is given in Fig. 7·23. In this example the lines AB and AC have the same length and *the development* may now be drawn as shown in Fig. 7·24.

Full Development

Now consider the development of the shape illustrated in Fig. 7·25. Although only a portion of the overall surface of the pyramid is required *it is convenient to reproduce the whole surface and then remove or delete the unwanted area.* From the orthographic views given in Fig. 7·26 the true length of the sloping edges are determined and the four isosceles triangles that represent the total surface of the pyramid are then drawn as shown in Fig. 7·27. The unwanted triangular areas are then deducted to obtain the actual development which is shown cross-hatched to avoid confusion.

Transition Pieces

A sheet-metal piece such as that shown in Fig. 7·25 enables a duct or tube of one size or shape to be joined to another of different size or shape so that the transition from the one to the other may be smooth and progressive. Such a piece is therefore termed a *Transition Piece.*

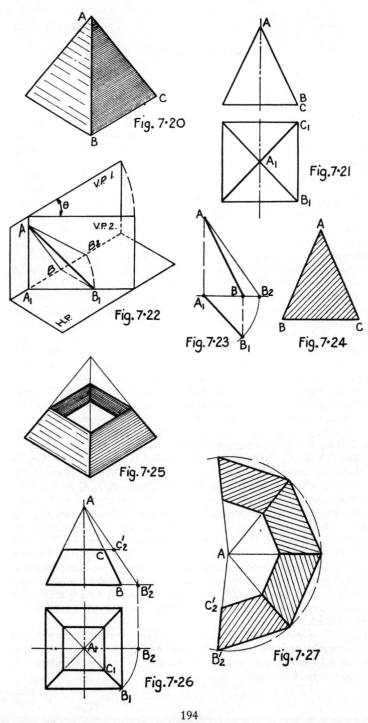

Fig. 7·20

Fig. 7·21

Fig. 7·22

Fig. 7·23

Fig. 7·24

Fig. 7·25

Fig. 7·26

Fig. 7·27

TRIANGULATION

Change in Shape

The problems so far examined have been capable of exact solution. In the case of the cylindrical tube and the hollow frustum of a cone a simple calculation enabled the true shape and area to be drawn, and with the transition piece made up from plane triangular surfaces the exact shape was readily determined, although in this instance the solution was entirely graphical. There are, in practice, many problems where the transition is from one shape to another of quite different form, such as from a circle to a rectangle, and in these cases the exact solution is so tedious that a graphical approximation is invariably used. A typical example which shows a rectangular sheet-metal air duct joined to a circular tube is illustrated in Fig. 7·28. The transition may be regarded as a combination of plane and curved surfaces, as suggested by the diagram, but the actual treatment assumes that the curved surfaces may also be "broken down" into triangular shapes as indicated pictorially in Fig. 7·29. The method of "break-down" should be carefully noted; first, there are four large triangular faces, each terminating at the circular end of the transition piece at points that are equally spaced round the circumference; the four quadrants thus produced are then divided into a number of small arcs which are joined to the adjacent corners of the rectangular end of the transition piece to form several long and narrow triangular shapes. The reduction of the whole surface into a series of triangular faces avoids warped or bent surfaces, and is referred to as *triangulation*.

The orthographic views of the piece are given in Fig. 7·30. The true lengths of the lines AP, AQ and AR are determined by revolving each of them in plan and projecting back into the elevation as previously demonstrated. An enlarged view of a portion of the transition piece is given in Fig. 7·31 so that the construction can be more clearly seen. The length of the line AS is already given in the elevation because its plan A_1S_1 is parallel with the vertical plane. To construct the narrow triangles APQ, AQR and ARS it is assumed that the small chords P_1Q_1, Q_1R_1 and R_1S_1 have the same length as their respective arcs. This assumption is obviously untrue, but the error introduced is regarded as sufficiently small to be neglected for most problems, providing the circular end is divided into at least twelve equal arcs. In the complete development shown in Fig. 7·32 it will be seen that the points P_1, Q_1, R_1 and S_1 have been joined with a smooth curve, and the whole surface has been drawn symmetrically about the large triangle ABS_1 with the opposite face divided equally. A symmetrical development generally saves material and by having the largest triangular face centrally disposed, as in Fig. 7·32 a further economy is often effected.

Fig. 7·33 shows the development of the same transition piece drawn symmetrically about the smaller triangular face AP_1D with the join along the line P_2H and in this instance the increase in the size of material is approximately 30 per cent.

195

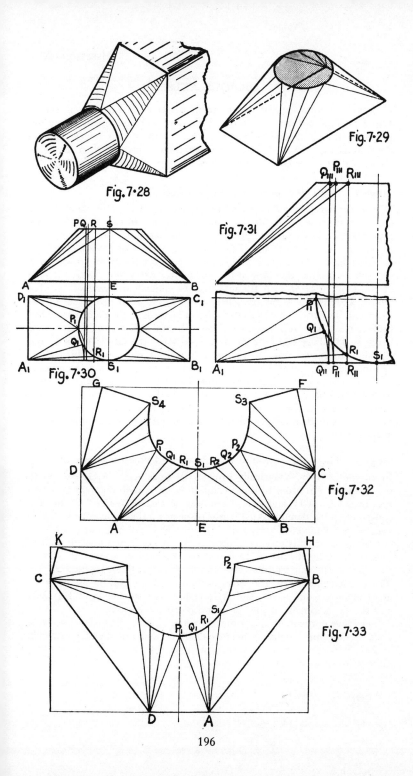

Fig. 7·28

Fig. 7·29

Fig. 7·31

Fig. 7·30

Fig. 7·32

Fig. 7·33

196

OBLIQUE AXES

A hollow oblique cone is cut to form a transition piece as shown at Fig. 7.34. Before describing in detail the method of treatment, it is again emphasized that the development is dealt with in two stages, by first developing the curved surface of the complete cone, and then removing from this the development of the unwanted portion above the line BC.

Stage 1   The Development of the Complete Cone

Divide the large circular end of the cone into twelve (or more) equal arcs and join the points of division $D_1F_1G_1$ etc. to the Apex A_1, thus dividing the whole surface into twelve triangular panels $A_1D_1F_1$, $A_1F_1G_1$ etc. as shown in plan at Fig. 7.34. These triangular pieces are clearly of different size, although being a symmetrical figure the triangles will have a duplicate on the other side of the axis of symmetry, but the true length of the long sides of each triangle may be quickly determined, as previously described, by rotating them in plan and then projecting to the elevation. The true lengths of the sides are shown in the elevation by the broken lines AF_2, AG_2 etc.; the lines AD and AE are, of course, true lengths. The base edge, or short side, of each triangle is taken as the chordal length subtended by each of the twelve circular arcs, this feature causing the solution to be approximate as in the preceding example.

The development is then carried out as shown at Fig. 7.35 commencing with the true shape of the triangular piece ADF_2, and then adding to this the true shape of the adjacent triangle AF_2G_2 and so on until the summation of the true shapes of all the triangular panels completes the development.

Stage 2   The Subtraction of the Unwanted Portion above BC

From the plan view vertically project the lines A_1F_1, A_1G_1 etc. on to the elevation. (In order to avoid congestion on a small diagram only two specimen lines A_1H_1 and A_1K_1 have been so treated in Fig. 7.34 and the construction is demonstrated with respect to these lines only.) The vertical projections of A_1H_1 and A_1K_1 are AH and AK and these lines cut BC at the points m and n respectively. A horizontal line through m cuts the true length line AH_2 at m_2 (see enlarged diagram Fig. 7.34A), Am_2 is thus the true length of Am. Similarly An_2 is the true length of An. These true lengths Am_2 and An_2 can then be marked off on the development along the lines AH_2 and AK_2 respectively as shown at Fig. 7.35 and the development of the transition piece completed.

The development of the same transition piece, drawn to the same scale, but arranged to give a short welded joint along the line CE is shown at Fig. 7.36. This arrangement effects a saving of material of approximately 20 per cent.

197

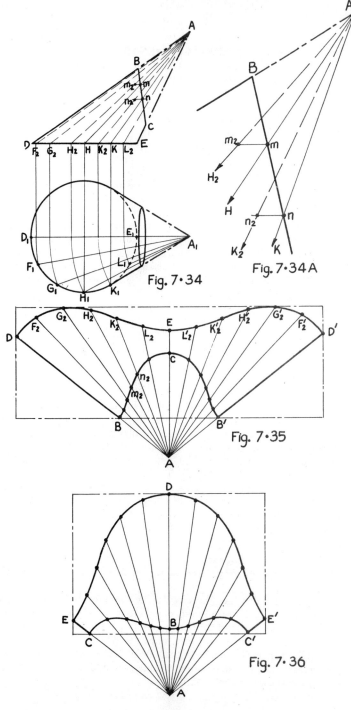

Fig. 7·34

Fig. 7·34 A

Fig. 7·35

Fig. 7·36

DEVELOPMENTS

Problems and Solutions

Example 1

A conical transition piece is cut to fit a circular tube as shown in Fig. 7·37. Develop the surface of the transition piece.

The upper edge of this piece has been reproduced in the plan for completeness, but in this instance the construction of this intersection curve is not essential to the development of the required surface. It should be noted that in many development problems it is necessary to plot such an intersection curve. By dividing the surface into twelve equal triangular pieces and plotting these by the approximate method the development of the whole cone is initially drawn. The true position of the points B_1, C_1, D_1 and E_1 is clearly indicated in the elevation, and the corresponding distances AB_2, AC_2, AD_2 and AE_2 are marked along the appropriate radial lines in Fig. 7·38 to enable the unwanted portion of the development to be removed. The points E_2, D_2, C_2 and B_2, etc., are joined by a smooth curve—*not by straight lines.*

Examples 2

Two cylindrical tubes of the same diameter interpenetrate as shown in Fig. 7·39, the axes of the tubes meeting at the point P. Develop the surface of tube A.

This problem demands the initial plotting of the intersection curves which, in this case, are straight lines. The partial plan in Fig. 7·39 enables the tube A to be divided into twelve parallel strips, all of the same width; the length of the vertical edges of these strips is given by the position of the points M, N, O, P, Q, R and S in the elevation.

In this case it is convenient to place the development beside the elevation so that the points M, N, O, etc., may be directly projected from Fig. 7·39 to Fig. 7·40. Establish the length of the complete cylinder using the approximate or exact method and divide this into twelve·equal parts, as shown. The projection of M, N, O, etc., to the appropriate vertical lines in Fig. 7·40 enables the development to be completed.

Example 3

The transition piece illustrated in Fig. 7·41 has an oblique axis and also involves a change in shape from a rectangle to a circle. Develop the surface.

Triangulate by dividing the circular end into twelve equal arcs and joining the points 0, 3, 6 and 9 respectively to A_1, B_1, C_1 and D_1 as shown. The intermediate points in the first quadrant are then joined to B_1, those in the second quadrant to C_1, etc., until the whole surface is "broken-down". The true outline of the triangle AOB is drawn first and, proceeding symmetrically, the remaining triangles are added above and below this shape as shown at Fig. 7·42.

199

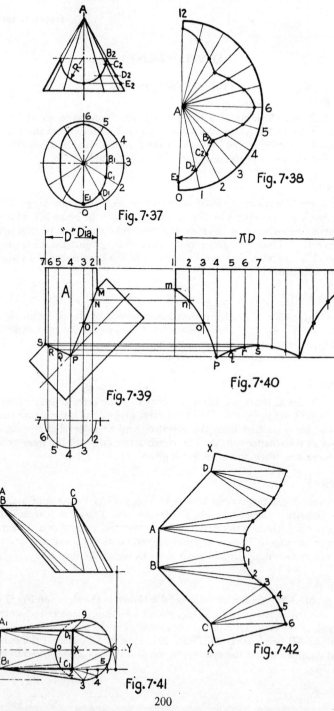

A

B₂
C₂
D₂
E₂

R

Fig. 7·37

6
5
4
B₁
3
C₁
2
E₁
D₁
O

12

A

B₂
C₂
D₂
E₂

6

5

4

3

2

1

O

Fig. 7·38

"D" Dia.

7 6 5 4 3 2 1

A

M
N
O

S
R Q P

1 2 3 4 5 6 7

m
n
o

P q r s

Fig. 7·39

ΠD

Fig. 7·40

7
6
5
4
3
2

A
B

A
B

C
D

A₁

9

D₁

O

1 C₁

3 4

5

6

X
Y

Fig. 7·41

X

D

A

B

o
1
2
3
4
5
6

C

X

Fig. 7·42

200

DEVELOPMENTS

Problem Assignments

Exercise 1

The plan and elevation of a sheet-metal transition piece are shown in Fig. 7·43. Draw the given views FULL SIZE and then develop the surface of the piece assuming that the joint in the material must be along the line XX. The thickness of the metal should be neglected.

Exercise 2

An oblique triangular pyramid is shown in Fig. 7·44, the views being First Angle projections. The object is to be cut by the plane XY which is parallel to the edge AB in elevation and perpendicular to the vertical plane of projection. Draw the given views FULL SIZE, project the plan of the surface XY and then develop the surfaces of the pyramid to the right of the section plane XY.

Exercise 3

Two oblique conical tubes are joined as indicated by the elevation shown in Fig. 7·45. Draw the given view FULL SIZE, project the plan and then develop the surface of that part of the transition piece marked X. The method of construction must be clearly shown.

Exercise 4

Two cylindrical tubes are joined as shown by the orthographic views in Fig. 7·46. Draw the given views FULL SIZE, project the intersection curve that has been omitted from the elevation and then develop the curved surface of the smaller tube A. The construction for both the intersection curve and the development must be given.

Exercise 5

The First Angle projections shown in Fig. 7·47 give details of a sheet-metal transition piece which has an oblique axis. The piece is required to join a rectangular duct to an elliptical tube that has a major axis of 62 mm and a minor axis of 50 mm. Draw the given views FULL SIZE and develop the surface assuming that the joint must be along the line XX.

Exercise 6

The profile ABC of a flat sheet of metal is shown in the elevation Fig. 7·48. This sheet is to be wrapped tightly round a 50 mm diameter rod so that the ends of the edge AB just meet as indicated in the given end view—the length of AB being 50π mm. Draw, FULL SIZE, an elevation of the sheet-metal wrapped round the cylindrical rod and project a plan beneath this elevation.

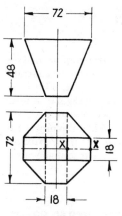

Fig. 7·43

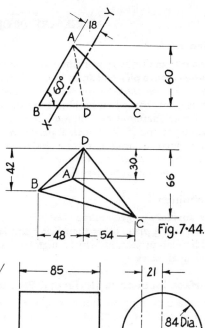

Fig. 7·44.

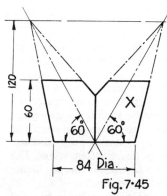

Fig. 7·45

85

45°

A

54

42 Dia.

21

84 Dia.

Fig. 7·46

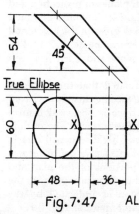

True Ellipse

Fig. 7·47

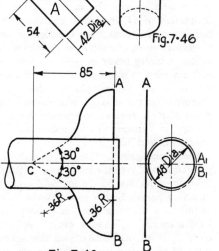

Fig. 7·48

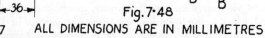

ALL DIMENSIONS ARE IN MILLIMETRES

202

AUXILIARY PROJECTION

General

As a rule an Ordinary workshop drawing gives three orthographic views—an elevation, a plan and an end view—and these three projections generally show the *true shape* of the three principal faces of the object. This is, of course, only true when the object drawn is essentially rectangular in form and may therefore be "placed" so that its three faces are respectively parallel to one of the principal planes of projection. When the object has an inclined surface (i.e. *surface that is not parallel with one of the principal planes of projection*), an *Auxiliary View* is necessary if the true shape of the inclined face is to be drawn.

Definition

An auxiliary projection may be defined as a projection upon an auxiliary plane (i.e. a plane other than V.P.1 and H.P. Fig. 8·2). It is generally an additional projection which augments the information given by the principal views.

Surface inclined to Horizontal Planes

A typical example is shown in Fig. 8·1, which illustrates a simple angle bracket that has one "limb" inclined at 45 degrees to the horizontal plane. It will be apparent that while the complete elevation can be immediately drawn, only the outline of the plan and end view may be thrown down, and neither of these views will show the true shape of the sloping face. To show the true shape of this surface it is necessary to project it upon a plane that is parallel with the surface. A line XY is therefore drawn with an inclination of 45 degrees to represent this new plane of projection and projectors are taken from the sloping face to this auxiliary plane. The projectors must, of course, be parallel with one another and perpendicular to the auxiliary plane in order to give a true representation of shape. A pictorial view of the object showing the principal planes of projection and the additional auxiliary plane is illustrated at Fig. 8·2; it should be noted that although the auxiliary plane is inclined at 45 degrees to the horizontal plane H.P. it remains perpendicular to the vertical plane V.P.1. The "hinge" or "ground line"¹ between the auxiliary plane and V.P.1 has been clearly marked XY.

Referring again to Fig. 8·1, it will be appreciated that the auxiliary projection will give the true shape of the sloping face because it is viewed from the direction of the arrow A—i.e. the surface is observed from a direction perpendicular to the plane containing the surface. The outline of this view may therefore be quickly reproduced because it will clearly have a length "L" and a width "W" *and the drilled hole will be drawn circular*. With this view drawn the unfinished portions of the plan and the end view may be rapidly thrown down, the elliptical views of the drilled holes being obtained by direct projection as indicated by the chordal dimension W_1 shown in the corresponding views of Fig. 8·1.

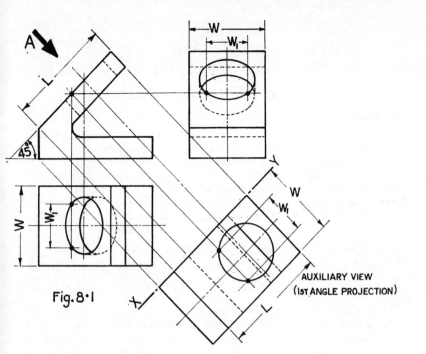

A

L

45°

W

W₁

W

W₁

Y

AUXILIARY VIEW
(1ST ANGLE PROJECTION)

W

W₁

X

Fig. 8·1

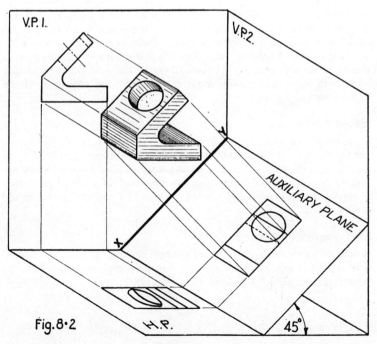

V.P. I.

V.P. 2.

AUXILIARY PLANE

Y

X

H.P.

45°

Fig. 8·2

204

POSITION OF AUXILIARY VIEWS

Purpose

The example that has just been examined is obviously a very simple case because there is only one inclined feature, and this is perpendicular to one of the principal planes. For this reason it may be said that all the necessary manufacturing information could be easily given without projecting an auxiliary view. Such a statement will now be recognized as a "half-truth" since even this simple case has demonstrated that an auxiliary view greatly facilitates the accurate projection of the normal orthographic views. Auxiliary views have, therefore, a twofold value:

(a) They enable the true shape of inclined surfaces to be shown.

(b) They permit the normal orthographic views to be rapidly projected.

Position

All four views of the angle bracket illustrated overleaf are clearly First Angle projections, and, in consequence, the distance between the elevation and the auxiliary view is considerable. To overcome this disadvantage, it is usual to *change the angle of projection of the auxiliary* and to place the view in a position adjacent to the surface it truly represents. This alternative position for an auxiliary view is shown in Fig. 8·3. The diagram illustrates another advantage that the adoption of this position confers—the auxiliary view is more readily related to the associated surface. An additional feature that is worthy of note is illustrated in Fig. 8·4 where the auxiliary view is symmetrical about an axis that is parallel with the ground line XY, it is only necessary to draw half the auxiliary view; this procedure saves both space and time without complicating the projection of the derived views.

Mixed Angle

To prevent confusion and ensure that the change in angle of projection is not overlooked, it is necessary to add the arrow to the ground line as shown in both Fig. 8·3 and 8·4; the very special circumstances are further emphasized by stating that this "mixing" of angle of projection is only accepted practice for auxiliary views—the *principal* views should not be mixed.

First Auxiliary Views

Where only one auxiliary is needed to show the true shape of an inclined surface and enable the principal views to be completed, the additional view is termed a *First Auxiliary Projection*.

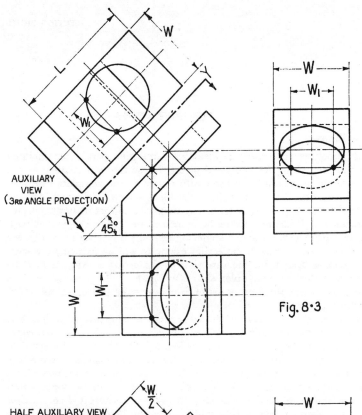

AUXILIARY
VIEW
(3RD ANGLE PROJECTION)

45°

Fig. 8·3

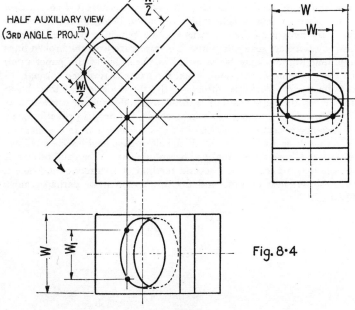

HALF AUXILIARY VIEW
(3RD ANGLE PROJ.ᵀᴺ)

Fig. 8·4

FIRST AUXILIARY VIEWS

New Plans

It is sometimes necessary to assemble a machine part in an inclined position relative to the associated pieces, i.e. so that a particular part is mounted in an auxiliary position with regard to the complete machine. For instance the "stepped" rectangular block shown by the orthographic views given in Fig. 8·5 may require to be placed so that its under surface is inclined at 45 degrees to the horizontal plane. Draw a new view with the base inclined at the stated angle, as shown by the elevation in Fig. 8·6 and the relationship with the earlier examples will be immediately seen. The plan as seen from the direction of the arrow A will, in fact, be identical with the original plan shown in Fig. 8·5. The plan of the block as seen from the direction of arrow B may now be projected, the width "W" being strictly maintained.

An alternative treatment of the same problem is illustrated in Fig. 8·7, the *new plan* being obtained by direct projection from the principal views originally given in Fig. 8·5. A ground line X_1Y_1 is drawn at 45 degrees to the initial ground line XY to represent the auxiliary plane and projectors are taken from all the "keypoints" in the elevation to meet this new plane. The use of a new term should be carefully noted; the auxiliary projection obtained in Fig. 8·7 has been labelled *"New Plan"* because it is a projection from an elevation, the direction of observation being indicated by the arrow C. By comparing the diagrams Fig. 8·6 and 8·7 it will be seen that the two solutions are really the same. To emphasize this, the broken lines surrounding Fig. 8·6 may be regarded as the edges of the paper upon which the views are drawn, and, when the paper is revolved through 45 degrees in an anti-clockwise direction, the three views will then be in approximately the same position as those in Fig. 8·7 *and the derived views will be identical.* Comparing the two methods, the first is probably more easier visualized because, in elevation, the object is shown in the inclined position that it has to occupy—while the alternative enables the auxiliary to be obtained from the normal orthographic views. When the profile of the object is complicated, the second method of treatment may save a considerable amount of time and for this reason it is, perhaps, more widely used.

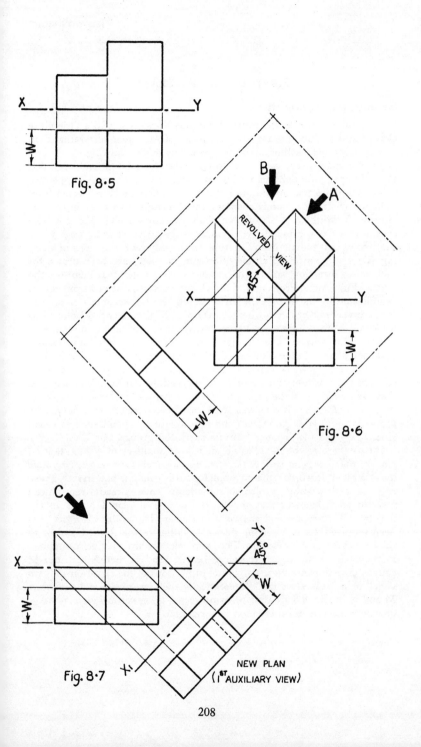

Fig. 8·5

REVOLVED VIEW

45°

Fig. 8·6

Fig. 8·7

NEW PLAN
(1ST AUXILIARY VIEW)

45°

208

FIRST AUXILIARY PLANS

Geometrical Approach

It is useful to examine the principles of auxiliary projection a little more closely, and to think for a moment in terms of solid geometry rather than of the direct approach of auxiliary views to machine drawing.

Theoretically, every view that is projected from an elevation is regarded as a plan and, although many of them may not have any real or practical value, it follows that an infinite number of plans may be projected from a single elevation by merely changing the direction of viewing, or the line of sight. A limited number of such plans are reproduced in Fig. 8·8. The central point O represents the position of the observer in all cases while the arrows that radiate from O represent the different directions of viewing. To avoid confusion an elevation and its plan have been drawn for each arrow direction, and it will be immediately noted that Plan A is the normal First Angle Projection of the object when it is viewed from above, as indicated by the arrow A. Plan B should also be recognized as similar to the preceding problem where a new plan of the "stepped" block was projected from the given elevation, arrow B indicating the direction of sight for this view. An examination of the other views shows quite clearly that each change in the direction of observation brings about a change in the projected view. A closer scrutiny reveals that these changes only concern the position and visibility of the various surfaces. The surfaces that are *visible* when the object is viewed from the direction of arrow B become *hidden* when it is viewed from the direction of arrow E, *but in both plans the width W is maintained* and the plan of any point such as P will always be the same distance from its particular ground line XY.

It may therefore be stated as a basic rule of auxiliary projection that *all plans of the same point must be the same distance from their respective ground lines*. While it is worth while to emphasize this rule it is not, in fact, a new rule of orthographic projection; students have already reproduced *inverted plans* such as that shown in Fig. 8·8 at plan D. And in the majority of examples and exercises in earlier chapters an end view has been required, the view being projected either to the Right Hand or to the Left Hand of the elevation. The same relationship must be maintained in these views and it can therefore be regarded as merely a matter of convenience to name these horizontal projections of the elevation an "end view" or a "side elevation"; theoretically they are plans, and the views M and N in Fig. 8·8 are thus plans projected upon *vertical ground lines—* or where the line of observation is horizontal.

209

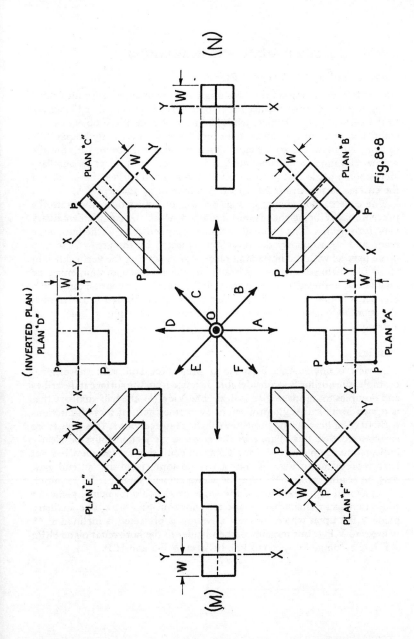

Fig. 8·8

210

FIRST AUXILIARY ELEVATIONS (1)

Surface Inclined to Vertical Plane

The simple angle bracket that was originally examined is again illustrated in Fig. 8·9, but in this instance the sloping surface is inclined at 45 degrees to the vertical plane. Hence, while the normal plan of the object can be completed without hesitation, the normal elevation can only be partially drawn. To show the true shape of the inclined surface and enable the normal elevation to be completed, it is necessary to project an auxiliary view upon a plane that is parallel with the inclined surface, i.e. a view of the surface as seen from the direction indicated by the arrow A.

The construction shown in Fig. 8·9 will be sufficient to illustrate the procedure, XY being the ground line upon which the complete auxiliary view is projected. The inclined surface is perpendicular to the horizontal plane and consequently the direction indicated by the arrow A is in a plane parallel with the horizontal plane. It follows that the vertical height H of the inclined surface, as stated in the normal elevation must be maintained in the auxiliary elevation, and similarly, the chordal dimension H_1 that is obtained from the auxiliary must be transferred to the normal elevation to enable the correct projection of the circular hole to be obtained.

Position

The view is obviously a First Angle projection, and as in the original example, the outline is a considerable distance from the surface it describes and occupies more space than is desirable. View (b), the half auxiliary that is drawn in Third Angle projection, overcomes both of these limitations without complicating the projection of the required views. It is once more emphasized that this change in the angle of projection must be clearly indicated in the manner shown. To avoid confusion an end view has not been reproduced in Fig. 8·9, but it will be appreciated that an end view may be readily projected from the views shown, should it be required.

A pictorial representation of the angle bracket, the principal planes of projection and the auxiliary plane are shown in Fig. 8·10. The auxiliary plane V.P.2 upon which the new elevation is projected is inclined at 45 degrees to V.P.1, but remains perpendicular to the horizontal plane H.P.: XY is the "hinge" or ground line between V.P.2 and H.P.

211

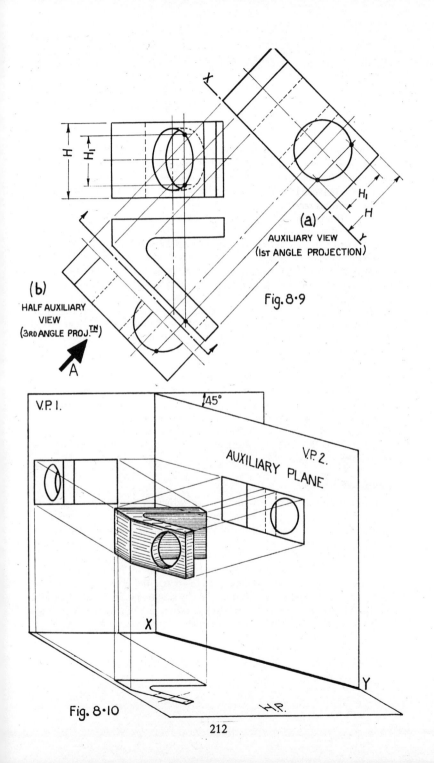

X

H

H₁

(a)

AUXILIARY VIEW
(1ST ANGLE PROJECTION)

Y

H₁

H

Fig. 8·9

(b)

HALF AUXILIARY
VIEW
(3RD ANGLE PROJ.ᵀᴺ)

A

V.P. I.

45°

V.P. 2.

AUXILIARY PLANE

X

Y

H.P.

Fig. 8·10

FIRST AUXILIARY ELEVATIONS (2)

New Elevations

The alternative problem in auxiliary projection must now be considered, i.e. *the case where the object as a whole must be placed so that its upright surfaces are inclined to the normal vertical plane of projection.* The simple "stepped" rectangular block with which we are already familiar will be re-introduced for this purpose. The normal orthographic views of this block are given in Fig. 8·11, but it will be assumed that the block is to be revolved in the horizontal plane until its vertical faces are all inclined at 45 degrees to the vertical plane, as indicated by the plan shown in Fig. 8·12. In this diagram the elevation projected upon the ground line X_1Y_1 is clearly a view of the block when it is observed from the direction of the arrow A. It should be apparent that this outline will be identical with the elevation given in Fig. 8·11 and that it is therefore a true image of shape. Thus, the dimension "H" which records the distance between the upper and lower surfaces is a true dimension. When this elevation is completed, the elevation, *as seen from the direction of the arrow B*, may be immediately projected. The upper surface of the block must be given the same vertical height "H" with respect to the corresponding ground line XY and, although it has been omitted from Fig. 8·12 it will be understood that the intermediate vertical dimension to the "step" must be the same in both elevations. Fig. 8·13 shows the solution obtained by direct projection from the given orthographic views, the direction of observation being indicated by the arrow C. Although the disposition of the views reproduced in Figs. 8·12 and 8·13 are somewhat different, the derived views are clearly identical.

Revolved Views

It is often found that, where there is difficulty in understanding the principles of auxiliary projection, the trouble quickly disappears when one thinks in terms of revolving the object about a horizontal or vertical axis with respect to the observer. When an observer walks completely round a building he will see many different elevations, but from every view point the height of the building will obviously be the same. It follows that if the direction of observation is regarded as fixed and the object is then rotated about a vertical axis, the result must be the same—i.e. in terms of a building the observer would see, one after another, the north, east, south and west faces, but all views would present the same maximum height.

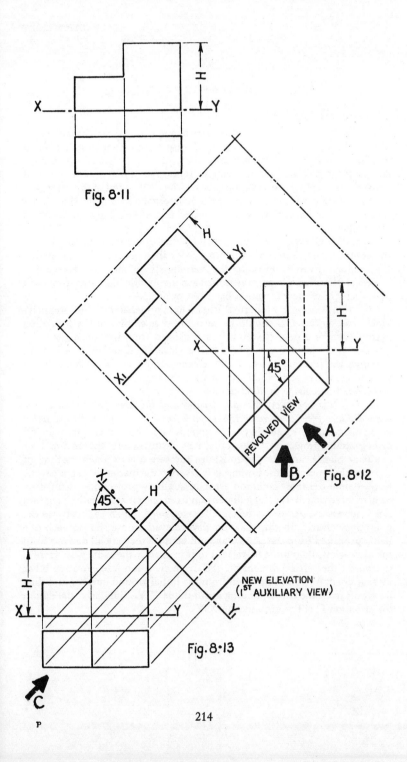

Fig. 8·11

Fig. 8·12

REVOLVED VIEW

45°

NEW ELEVATION
(1ST AUXILIARY VIEW)

45°

Fig. 8·13

214

P

FIRST AUXILIARY ELEVATIONS (3)

Geometrical Approach

Reviewing the matter from a geometrical stand-point, all views that are projected from a plan are regarded as elevations and from a single plan an infinite number of elevations may therefore be projected by merely changing the direction of observation. It should be noted, however, that while the direction of observation may be from "any point of the compass" the line of sight will, in every case, be horizontal and it is for this reason that *vertical dimensions remain unchanged* regardless of the direction of observation.

Several new elevations have been reproduced in Fig. 8·14. In all cases the central point represents the position of the observer and the arrows that radiate from it indicate the various directions of observation. Identical plans have been drawn for each arrow direction and from each plan the derived new elevation has been projected.

Elevation A is clearly a normal First Angle projection of the "stepped" block, and elevation B should be recognized as similar to the preceding example where a new elevation was projected from the given plan. All the elevations have a difference, but a close examination reveals that, although the position and visibility of the various surfaces change from view to view, the vertical dimensions are the same in all of them, i.e. *the height "H" is common in all elevations.*

It may thus be stated that *all elevations of the same point ·must be the same distance from their respective ground lines.* Once again, this is not a new rule peculiar to auxiliary drawing; it is fundamentally true for all orthographic projection. The only new features are the inclined or auxiliary planes, and the ground lines that are a convenient method of representing such planes. Emphasis is given to the matter in an endeavour to overcome the most common error in auxiliary projection—it must be remembered that to transfer a dimension from one view to another a datum line is necessary, *and this datum is a "ground line".* Fig. 8·15 illustrates the point very clearly. In this diagram three elevations are shown, each one being projected from the same plan, and because they are all derived from the same view, they must be related to it in exactly the same way. Hence, to transfer the vertical dimension "H" from elevation A to elevation B the measurement must first be taken from the initial ground line XY and then be set off from the corresponding ground line X_1Y_1. Similarly, the datum for elevation C is the ground line X_2Y_2.

215

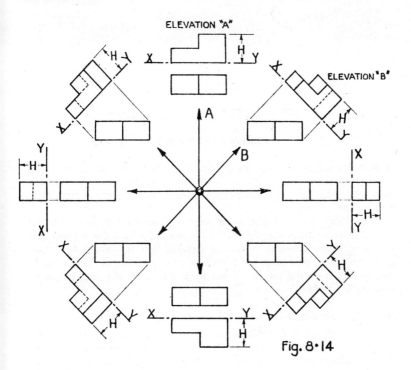

ELEVATION "A"

ELEVATION "B"

Fig. 8·14

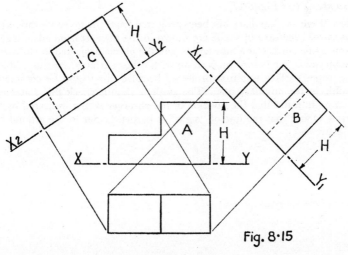

Fig. 8·15

216

FIRST AUXILIARY PROJECTION

Problems and Solutions

It may be regarded as unnecessary to further demonstrate the projection of First Auxiliary views, but in the following examples curved surfaces have been introduced and it is perhaps necessary to show how easily these may be dealt with.

Complexity of outline does not change the method of procedure in any way, it merely entails the projection of additional points, the number used being sufficient to define the actual surfaces that are involved. In both examples the construction has been kept to a minimum so that it can be clearly seen that the points chosen to delineate an irregular shape are selected at random.

Example 1 (*see* Fig. 8·16)

In this case the curved surface is described in the given elevation and the auxiliary projected is a New Elevation. While the points A, B and C are chosen arbitrarily, they must be selected in positions of maximum usefulness, and the usual practice is to initially project no more than three or four points and subsequently to add a few more where they will obviously be most useful.

Example 2 (*see* Fig. 8·17)

Here the First Auxiliary has been projected from the given elevation and the curved features of shape are shown in the plan. It is an advantage to project one surface at a time and to join the points projected in alphabetic (numeric) order before proceeding with other surfaces. In this instance the upper surface was first projected because this would be completely visible in the auxiliary plan. The student should check this statement, bearing in mind that the position of the observer is that indicated by the arrow Q and that the line of "sight" is perpendicular to the ground line X_1Y_1.

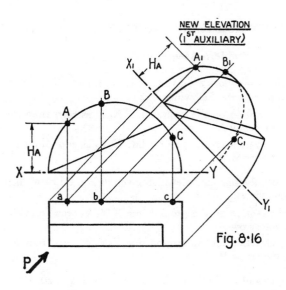

NEW ELEVATION
(1ST AUXILIARY)

Fig. 8·16

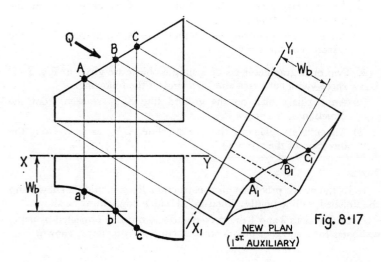

NEW PLAN
(1ST. AUXILIARY)

Fig. 8·17

218

FIRST AUXILIARY PROJECTION

Problem Assignments

1. The principal views of a block are given in Fig. 8·18. Draw these views FULL SIZE and then project the following:

   (a) An auxiliary elevation on the ground line $X_A Y_A$ as seen from the direction of the arrow A.

   (b) An auxiliary elevation on the ground line $X_B Y_B$ as seen from the direction of the arrow B.

2. Draw, FULL SIZE, the plan and elevation given in Fig. 8·19 and then project the following views:

   (a) An auxiliary elevation on the ground line $X_A Y_A$ as seen from the direction of the arrow A.

   (b) An auxiliary elevation on the ground line $X_B Y_B$ as seen from the direction of the arrow B.

3. First Angle views of a "Vee" block are shown in Fig. 8·20. Draw these views FULL SIZE and then project the following:

   (a) An auxiliary plan on the ground line $X_P Y_P$ as seen, from the direction of the arrow P.

   (b) An auxiliary plan on the ground line $X_Q Y_Q$ as seen from the direction of the arrow Q.

4. Two orthographic views of a simple object are given in Fig. 8·21. Draw these views FULL SIZE and then project the following:

   (a) An auxiliary plan on the ground line $X_P Y_P$ as seen from the direction of the arrow P.

   (b) An auxiliary plan on the ground line $X_Q Y_Q$ as seen from the direction of the arrow Q.

NOTES

1. In the above problems all construction lines should be shown and the finished outline boldly "lined-in". Hidden edges must be shown.

2. In Exercises 2 and 4 the curved surfaces must be projected by using ordinates for a series of points on each curve, as previously shown.

219

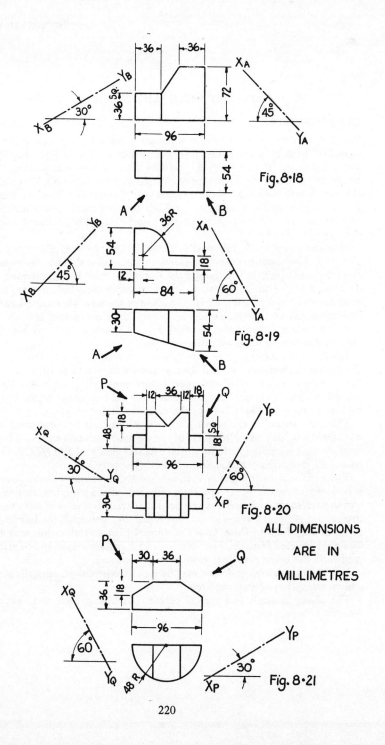

Fig. 8·18

Fig. 8·19

Fig. 8·20

ALL DIMENSIONS
ARE IN
MILLIMETRES

Fig. 8·21

220

SECOND AUXILIARY VIEWS

Oblique Surfaces

We have seen that where an inclined surface is perpendicular to one of the principal planes, one of the principal views of the object may be immediately drawn and, with the aid of a *single auxiliary projection*, the remaining principal views may be completed without difficulty. When the sloping surface is *inclined to the two principal planes* it becomes necessary to project two auxiliary views to establish the true shape of the oblique surface and none of the principal views may be completed without using the auxiliary views.

The procedure to be followed in these circumstances is illustrated in Fig. 8·22. The diagram shows the simple angle bracket that has been used in earlier examples, but, although the sloping "limb" is still inclined at 45 degrees to the horizontal plane, in this instance the whole bracket has been revolved to a position where the edges of the base are inclined at 45 degrees to the vertical plane. Consequently, the sloping face is inclined to the two normal planes of projection. Fig. 8·23 will no doubt enable this oblique position to be more easily visualized.

It will be appreciated that initially only a few lines may be drawn for the plan and elevation—and, in fact, it is only necessary to throw down the rectangular outline of the plan before proceeding with the First Auxiliary view. This auxiliary elevation gives the true shape of the angle bracket when it is observed from the direction of arrow A.

The true shape of the sloping surface is obtained by projecting an additional auxiliary which must clearly be a projection upon a ground line, or plane, that is parallel with the surface. As this view is *A PROJECTION from a First Auxiliary it is called a Second Auxiliary.*

The surface is assumed to be symmetrical about a longitudinal axis and it is therefore necessary to reproduce only half of the complete outline—and in agreement with present practice the partial view is in Third Angle projection. A limited amount of the remaining construction has been given in Fig. 8·22 to show how the normal plan and elevation may be directly projected from the First and Second Auxiliary views, and to avoid confusion the other principal view has been omitted.

It is obvious that an end view may be rapidly reproduced once the plan and elevation has been completed.

The above example is a typical problem involving First and Second Auxiliary Projections.

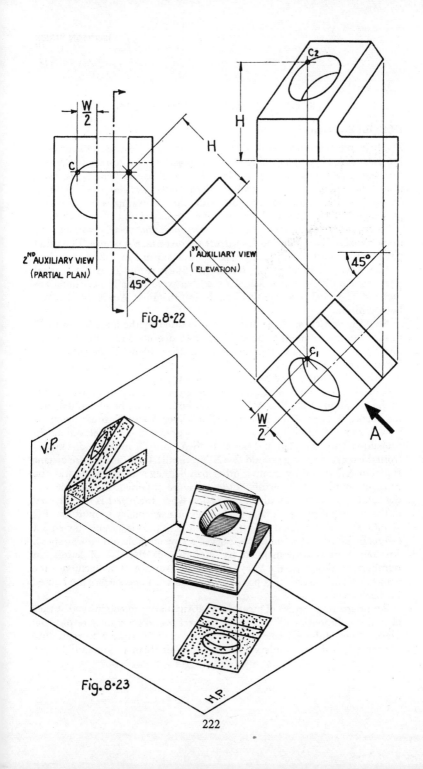

W/2

C

2ND AUXILIARY VIEW
(PARTIAL PLAN)

H

1ST AUXILIARY VIEW
(ELEVATION)

45°

Fig. 8·22

C₂

H

45°

C₁

W/2

A

V.P.

Fig. 8·23

H.P.

222

SECOND AUXILIARY PROJECTION

Oblique Position

To complete this study of auxiliary projection it is necessary to consider the case of an object placed in an oblique position with respect to the two principal planes—i.e. *so that horizontal surfaces are inclined to the horizontal plane and vertical surfaces inclined to the vertical planes*; and to enable an immediate comparison with earlier examples in auxiliary projection the "stepped" block will be employed once again and, in addition, it will be assumed that the horizontal and vertical surfaces are to be respectively inclined at 45 degrees to the principal planes. The usual orthographic views of the object are reproduced in Fig. 8·24.

The elevation in Fig. 8·25 shows the block revolved in the vertical plane to a position where the surfaces that were initially horizontal are inclined at 45 degrees. To avoid confusion the First Auxiliary plan has been omitted.

Now the vertical surfaces that are represented by the lines AB and CD in the plan are required to be inclined at 45 degrees and hence a ground line X_1Y_1 must be drawn to indicate the auxiliary plane. X_1Y_1 will thus be inclined at 45 degrees to AB and CD, and the direction of observation that is indicated by the arrow M is perpendicular to X_1Y_1.

Considering the edges of the block one by one, it will be apparent that as the elevation of the line AC is a *point* the line must be horizontal, and the vertical height of the two ends of the line, A and C, must therefore be the same. This condition must be maintained in all elevations in projection with the plan and hence both A_1 and C_1 must be distant H_1 from the corresponding ground line X_1Y_1. Similarly, B_1 and D_1 are distant H_2 from X_1Y_1, and by treating other parallel edges in the same way the complete outline of the auxiliary view may be obtained. Fig. 8·26 shows the solution obtained by direct projection when the *object* is not inclined to the principal planes. The introduction of a secondary ground line PQ should be carefully noted; *PQ is parallel to X_1Y_1*. It is a more convenient reference plane and in addition it saves a considerable amount of space. Another feature demonstrated by Fig. 8·26 is the use of letters, or numbers, to designate the "key" points of a surface. This facilitates the projection and ensures that points concerned with one surface are jointed in the correct order.

An interesting feature of most Second Auxiliary projections is that they are "three-dimensional" and appear, therefore, to be similar to pictorial views. They differ by the fact that it is usually desirable to reproduce hidden edges in an auxiliary view but to omit them in a pictorial view.

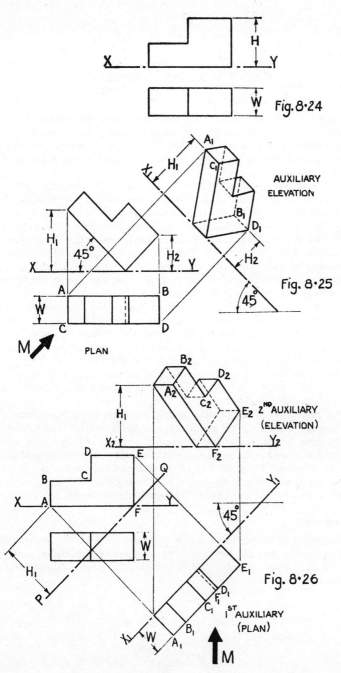

H

X — — — — — — — — Y

W   Fig. 8·24

A₁

H₁

X

C₁

AUXILIARY
ELEVATION

B₁

D₁

H₁

45°

H₂

X — — — — Y

H₂

45°

Fig. 8·25

H₂

A   B

W

C   D

M

PLAN

B₂

D₂

A₂

H₁

C₂

E₂ 2ⁿᵈ AUXILIARY
(ELEVATION)

X₂   Y₂

F₂

D   E

B   C   Q

X   Y₁

A   F

45°

H₁

W

E₁

P

Fig. 8·26

X₁   D₁
F₁
C₁   1ˢᵗ AUXILIARY
(PLAN)

W   B₁

A₁

M

224

SECOND AUXILIARY PROJECTION

Visible and Hidden Surfaces

It is generally considered necessary to show hidden edges and surfaces in an auxiliary view. This requirement seldom presents any difficulty when the projection is a first auxiliary, but there is often considerable doubt when trying to discriminate between the visible and hidden surfaces of a second auxiliary.

In all previous examples an arrowhead was boldly marked to indicate the position of the observer, and it is strongly recommended that this practice is adopted for all problems in auxiliary projection. Furthermore, the student should try to imagine himself occupying the position indicated by the arrow and endeavour to visualize the outline of the object when it is observed from this direction. This procedure, coupled with the idea of regarding the object as revolved with respect to the principal planes, will often resolve any difficulty, but when there is still uncertainty the following method will always clarify the situation.

In Fig. 8·27 first and second auxiliary projections of a simple object have been reproduced, the arrow A indicating the direction of observation for obtaining the final auxiliary view. Two "key" points, P_1 and Q_1, have been marked on the auxiliary plan, P_1 being the point that is *nearest to the observer* and Q_1 the point that is *furthest from the observer*.

The projection of P_1 to the second ground line X_2Y_2 determines the position of the point P_2 which will be *common to three visible faces*—i.e. the point where three visible faces meet.

The projection of Q_1 to the second auxiliary view determines the position of the point Q_2 the point that is *common to three hidden faces*.

The same rule may of course be applied to first auxiliary views, but it will no doubt be appreciated that as first auxiliaries are "two-dimensional" instead of "three" the projection of the near and remote points will give *a line that is respectively common to the visible and hidden surfaces*. It is clearly impossible to have a line that is common to three different surfaces.

Summary

When projecting from a first auxiliary to a second, the point nearest to the observer determines the junction between the visible surfaces, and the point remote from the observer determines the junction between the hidden surfaces.

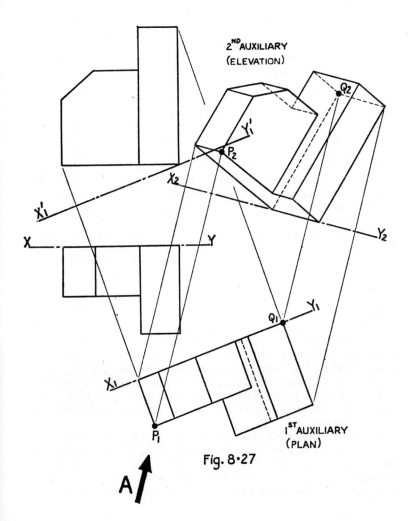

2ND AUXILIARY
(ELEVATION)

1ST AUXILIARY
(PLAN)

Fig. 8·27

226

SECOND AUXILIARY VIEWS

Posture

Although the subject of Auxiliary Projection has been adequately covered in the previous pages, the authors feel that the discerning student may find the following notes on "Posture" interesting and informative.

Order of Procedure

When the foregoing exercises have been completed, it will be realized that the order of procedure is of some importance. In a given problem the order of procedure will, of course, be defined by the statement that the second auxiliary view must be either an elevation or a plan—and in a practical application of auxiliary projection the final view that the case demands will equally describe the way to proceed. It follows that where the second auxiliary is required to be an *elevation* the first auxiliary must be a *plan* and, in turn, this view must be derived from an elevation. Thus, to obtain a second auxiliary elevation it is necessary to commence operations by projecting from another elevation, and similarly where the second auxiliary must be a plan the first step will be a projection from another plan.

While the *modus operandi* will normally be stated in this manner, there is an associated feature that is neither mentioned nor recognized as implied by the instructions. This feature concerns the difference in posture that is dependent upon whether the second auxiliary is an elevation or a plan.

Posture

A careful examination and comparison between the diagrams shown in Figs. 8·28 and 8·29 will reveal this difference. In Fig. 8·28 the second auxiliary is an elevation and this view shows the object tilted or inclined about one of its base edges, i.e. *about an edge that was originally in the horizontal plane*. In this instance the edge is lettered AB in the final view; this corresponds with the edge in the original elevation that is in contact with the subsidiary ground line X_1Y_1 and is, therefore, a hidden edge in the first auxiliary.

In Fig. 8·29 the second auxiliary is a plan and in this case the object is revolved or inclined about one of its vertical edges, i.e. *about an edge that was originally in the vertical plane*. The original plan shows this edge in contact with the subsidiary ground line X_1Y_1 and, as one should expect, this edge will show the junction between hidden surfaces in the first auxiliary.

Summary

(1) A second Auxiliary Elevation will show an object inclined about an edge that was originally in the horizontal plane, the edge being a hidden line in the first auxiliary view.

(2) A second Auxiliary Plan will show an object inclined about an edge that was originally in the vertical plane, the edge being a hidden line in the first auxiliary view.

227

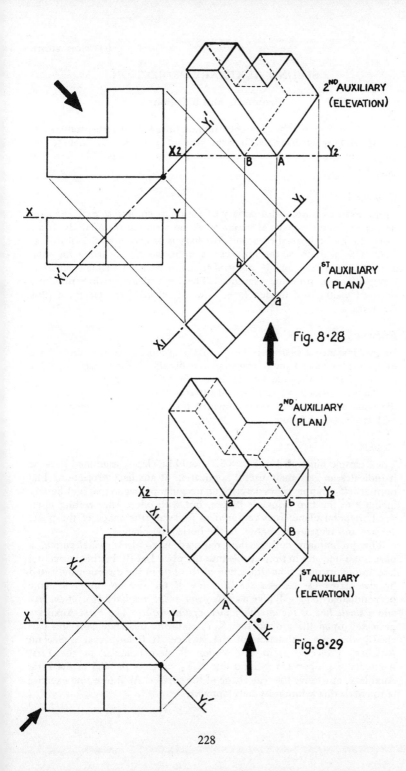

2ND AUXILIARY
(ELEVATION)

Y'

X₂   B   A   Y₂

X   Y   Y₁

X'

1ST AUXILIARY
(PLAN)

b

a

X₁

Fig. 8·28

2ND AUXILIARY
(PLAN)

X₂   a   b   Y₂

X₁

X'

B

1ST AUXILIARY
(ELEVATION)

X   Y

A

Y₁

Y'

Fig. 8·29

228

SECOND AUXILIARY PROJECTION

Problems and Solutions

To avoid confusion only a few construction lines have been reproduced in the accompanying diagrams, but the student is advised to examine the projections carefully and to add further construction should he find this necessary.

Example 1

In this example a Second Auxiliary Elevation is required so projectors are first taken from the given elevation to obtain a *plan as the First Auxiliary View*. From this plan the Second Auxiliary is projected as shown in Fig. 8·30. The position of the observer is indicated by an arrow for each projection and the "major" point of junction between visible surfaces is "ringed" as in previous examples. The importance of discriminating between visible and hidden faces is demonstrated very clearly in this diagram.

Example 2

In this instance a plan is required in the second projection and hence projectors are taken from the given plan to obtain the First Auxiliary. This new elevation is then used to derive the Second Auxiliary.

The method of projecting curved surfaces has been discussed earlier in the book and should be re-examined if the outlines reproduced in Fig. 8·31 are not understood.

Example 3

The example illustrated in Fig. 8·32 should be closely examined because it indicates an extremely useful application of auxiliary projection. The normal orthographic views describe an irregular pentagon that is obliquely inclined to the two principle planes, but with one corner resting upon the horizontal plane. It is required to find the true shape of the plane surface and its true inclination to the horizontal plane.

The preliminary construction required is to draw, *in elevation*, a horizontal line and to project this into the plan. Let BP be this horizontal line and *bp* its plan. The projection of this line in the direction indicated by the arrow Q—i.e.—*in the direction of the line bp*—upon a plane perpendicular to *bp* will give a *single point as the auxiliary view of the line* and a *single line as the auxiliary view of the surface*. The First Auxiliary projected upon the ground line X_1Y_1 confirms this statement and θ is clearly the true inclination of the surface. It follows that a Second Auxiliary projected from a direction R perpendicular to the First Auxiliary, i.e. upon the ground line X_2Y_2 which is parallel to the First Auxiliary, must give the true shape of the surface. An interesting exercise is to check this solution by development.

229

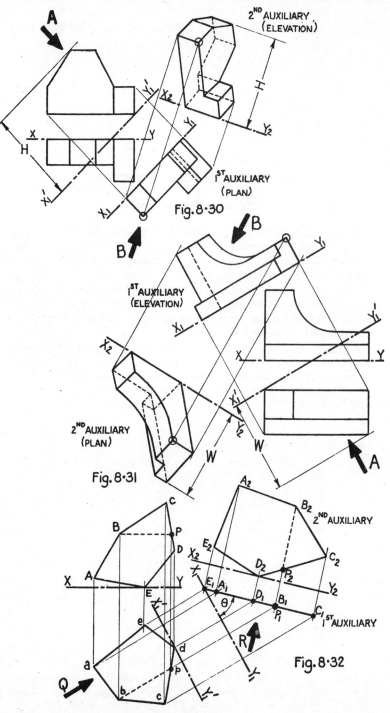

A

2ND AUXILIARY
(ELEVATION)

X₂

Y

X₂

H

X

Y

1ST AUXILIARY
(PLAN)

Y₂

H

X₁

X₁

B

Fig. 8·30

B

B

Y₁

1ST AUXILIARY
(ELEVATION)

X₁

Y'

X₂

X

Y

X'₁

Y₂

2ND AUXILIARY
(PLAN)

W

W

A

Fig. 8·31

A₂

c

B₂ 2ND AUXILIARY

B

P

E₂

D

D₂ P₂ C₂

X

A

E

Y

X₂

Y₂

e

X'₁

E₁ A₁

D₁ B₁

C₁ 1ST AUXILIARY

θ

d

P₁

a

R

Fig. 8·32

b

c

p

Q

Y₁

Ω

230

SECOND AUXILIARY PROJECTION

Problem Assignments

1. Draw, FULL SIZE, the orthographic views given in Fig. 8·33 and then project a New Elevation on the ground line X_1Y_1. From this auxiliary view project a Second Auxiliary on the ground line X_2Y_2. All hidden detail must be shown.

2. Draw, FULL SIZE, the plan and elevation shown in Fig. 8·34 and then project a First Auxiliary plan on the ground line X_1Y_1. From this plan project a Second Auxiliary on the ground line X_2Y_2. Essential construction and all hidden edges must be shown.

3. The Bearing Block illustrated by the views given in Fig. 8·35 must be drawn FULL SIZE. From the plan project a First Auxiliary Elevation on the ground line X_1Y_1 and from this view project a Second Auxiliary on the ground line X_2Y_2. Construction lines may be deleted but all hidden surfaces must be shown.

231

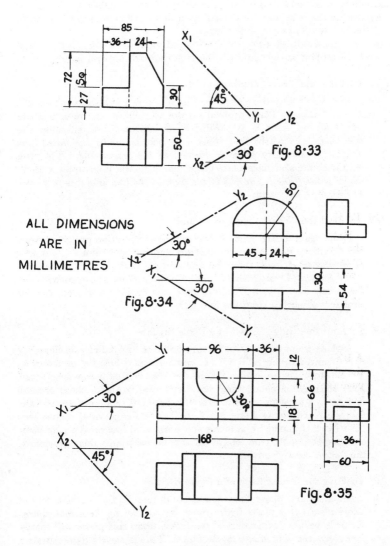

85
36 24
72 50 27
X₁
45°
Y₁ Y₂
30
50
X₂ 30° Fig. 8·33

ALL DIMENSIONS
ARE IN
MILLIMETRES

Y₂ 50
30°
X₂ X₁
45 24
30°
30
54
Fig. 8·34
Y₁

Y₁ 96 36 12
66
30°
X₁ 30R
X₂ 18
45° 168 36
60
Y₂ Fig. 8·35

AUXILIARY PROJECTION
(Line and Plane Problems)

The principles of auxiliary projection may be applied to give simple graphical solutions to line and plane problems. Auxiliary planes are selected so that the views projected upon them will contain one, or more, of the following items of information:
(a) the true length of a line, (b) the "point view" of a line, (c) the "edge view" of a plane surface and (d) the true shape of a plane figure.

(a) To Find the True Length of a Line.

Fig. 8·36 shows the elevation, $a'b'$, of a line and also its plan $a''b''$. A 1st Auxiliary Plan, projected from the elevation, upon a plane *whose ground line X_1Y_1 is parallel to the elevation $a'b'$* will show the *true length AB* of the line. This is so because *under the stated conditions the auxiliary plane is parallel to the actual line.* The true length could also have been projected from the plan upon a plane *whose ground line is parallel to the plan of the line* and this is shown at Fig. 8·37.

(b) To Find the "Point View" of a Line.

Refer again to Fig. 8·36. A 2nd Auxiliary Elevation projected from the Auxiliary Plan AB upon a plane whose ground line X_2Y_2 *is perpendicular to AB* will show the line as a point ab. This is so because *under the stated conditions the 2nd Auxiliary Plane is perpendicular to the actual line.* Fig. 8·37 shows how the "point view", cd, can be similarly projected from the line CD.

(c) To Find the "Edge View" of a Plane Surface

A plane triangular surface is represented at Fig. 8·38 by its elevation $A'B'C'$ and its plan $A''B''C''$. If *any horizontal line* $d'e'$ is drawn in the elevation its projection DE in the plan will be a *true length* (see page 189). An auxiliary view projected upon a plane whose ground line X_1Y_1 is perpendicular to DE will show DE as a point de, and the triangle therefore as a line $A'''B'''C'''$. The "edge view" could also have been obtained by drawing any horizontal line on the *plan* view and projecting its true length on the *elevation* and then projecting the "edge view" from the elevation.

(d) To Find the True Shape of a Plane Figure.

An auxiliary plane having a ground line X_2Y_2 *parallel to the "edge view"* of a plane figure must be *parallel to the actual figure.* An orthographic projection of the figure upon this plane will therefore show the true shape of the figure. This is clearly demonstrated by the 2nd Auxiliary Plan in Fig. 8·38.

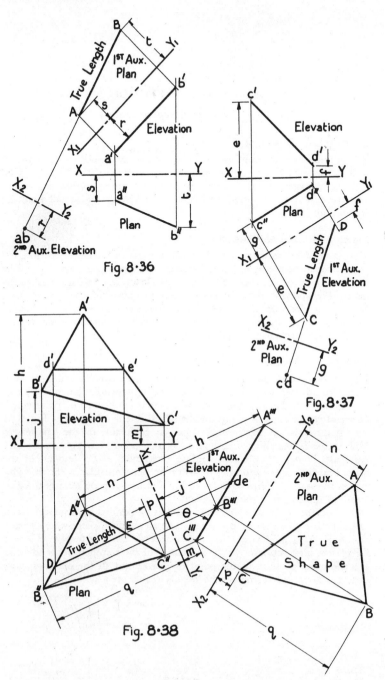

Fig. 8·36

Fig. 8·37

Fig. 8·38

AUXILIARY PROJECTION

(The Common Perpendicular)

Lines which Intersect

If one line intersects another the cross-over of the two lines in elevation will be in vertical projection with the cross-over of the lines in plan This is illustrated at Fig. 8·39 where p' and p" are in vertical alignment, and, represent in elevation and plan respectively, the actual point of intersection.

Lines which do not Intersect

If two lines *do not* intersect then the cross-over in elevation and the cross-over in plan *will not* be in vertical alignment (see Fig. 8·40). The problem now becomes one of finding how closely one line approaches the other. The shortest distance between any two straight lines which cross, but do not intersect, is measured in a direction mutually perpendicular to both lines. In other words the shortest link between two straight lines, which do not intersect, is their common perpendicular.

To Find the Common Perpendicular

Fig. 8·40 shows the plan and elevation of two lines which do not intersect. The method used to determine the common perpendicular to these two lines is illustrated at Fig. 8·41. The first step is to obtain the "point view" of *one* of the lines, it does not matter which line is selected. In Fig. 8·41 the "point view" gh has been obtained by projecting (a) the true length GH on the 1st Auxiliary Plane and (b) the "point view" gh on the 2nd Auxiliary Plane. The corresponding projection, e'''f''' and ef, of the other line are also drawn in. The common perpendicular is the line ghp drawn through gh perpendicular to ef. The line ghp represents the *true length* of the common perpendicular.

To find the point at which the common perpendicular intersects each line a further view may be projected upon an auxiliary plane *whose ground line X_3Y_3 is parallel to ef*. This view records the *true lengths HG and EF of both lines* and also the "point view" of the common perpendicular and the exact position of the point of intersection of the common perpendicular with each line can be readily scaled off.

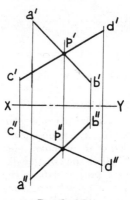

Fig. 8·39

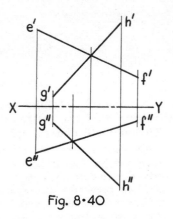

Fig. 8·40

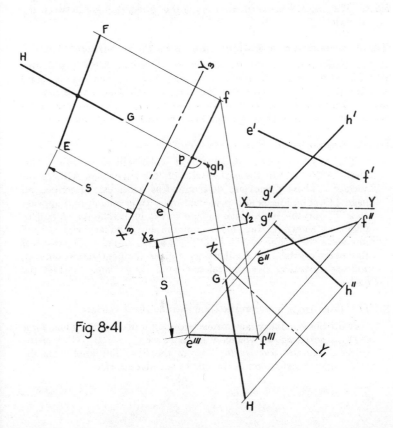

Fig. 8·41

236

AUXILIARY PROJECTION
(Line and Plane Problems)

To Find the Dihedral Angle between Two Plane Surfaces

Two plane surfaces are represented in elevation (a'b'c'd') and plan (a''b''c''d'') at Fig. 8·42. A 1st Auxiliary view is projected upon a plane whose ground line X_1Y_1 is parallel to the elevation of the common edge a'c'. As previously demonstrated, this view will show the true length, AC, of this common edge. (Alternatively a view projected from the *plan* upon a plane whose ground line is parallel to a''c'' will also show the true length AC.) A 2nd Auxiliary view, projected upon a plane whose ground line X_2Y_2 is perpendicular to AC, will show the projection of the common edge as a point ac and the surfaces dac and bac as straight lines. The angle θ between the lines is the dihedral angle between the two surfaces.

The Intersection of a Straight Line and a Plane Surface

A transparent plane surface is shown in elevation, A'B'C', and plan A''B''C'' at Fig. 8·43. A straight line, also shown in the elevation (g''h') and the plan (g''h''), penetrates the surface. Auxiliary views may be used to find (a) the position of the point at which the line penetrates the surface, and (b) the true angle between the line and the surface.

(a) The Position of the Penetration Point

The Auxiliary planes used are those which will give (1) the "edge view" A'''B'''C''' of the surface and (2) the true shape ABC of the surface. These planes are determined as previously described on page 233. The line is also projected upon these planes and appears as g'''h''' on the 1st Auxiliary plane and as gh on the 2nd Auxiliary plane, as shown at Fig. 8·43. On the 1st Auxiliary view g'''h''' intersects the "edge view" A'''B'''C''' at p', and the projection of this point on the 2nd Auxiliary view gives the penetration point p, and also gives its position relative to the *true shape* ABC of the surface.

(b) The True Angle between the Line and the Plane Surface

A further Auxiliary view projected upon a plane *whose ground line X_3Y_3 is parallel to gh* will show an "edge view", A''''B''''C'''', of the surface, and the *true length*, GH, of the line. The angle   is the true angle of inclination of the line to the plane surface.

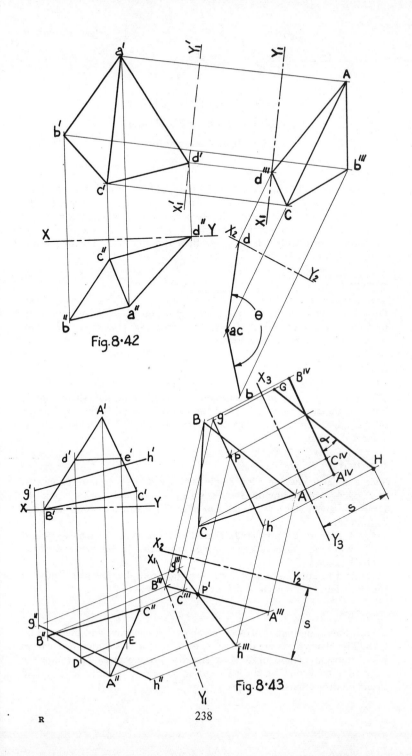

Fig. 8·42

Fig. 8·43

AUXILIARY PROJECTION
(Line and Plane Problems)
Problem Assignments

Exercise 1

The elevation (a'b' and c'd') and the plan (a''b'' and c''d'') of two lines are shown at Fig. 8·44. Draw FULL SIZE the given views and find (1) the length of their common perpendicular and (2) the position of the points of intersection of the common perpendicular and each line. Insert the common perpendicular on the given plan and elevation. The diagram is in First Angle Projection.

Exercise 2

Two lines are shown in elevation (e'f'g') and plan (e''f''g'') at Fig. 8·45. Draw, FULL SIZE, the given views and, by means of auxiliary projection, find the true length of each line and the true angle between them. The diagram is in First Angle Projection.

Exercise 3

The elevation (A'B'C'D') of two plane surfaces is shown at Fig. 8·46. The true length (AC) of the common edge is 140 mm, the dihedral angle between the surfaces is 270°, and the elevation A'D' is the true length of this edge. Draw FULL SIZE the given elevation and below this view project the plan.

Exercise 4

Two auxiliary views, in First Angle Orthographic Projection, illustrated at Fig. 8·47, show a line de intersecting a plane surface ABC at a point P. Draw the given views FULL SIZE and in addition project two other views as follows:

(1) A Plan to be projected from the Auxiliary View whose ground line is X_1Y_1—the direction of viewing is indicated by the arrow Z which is at 90° to X_1Y_1.

(2) An Elevation to be projected vertically from the new plan. Indicate the position of P on each of the additional views.

Exercise 5

Two intersecting plane surfaces are shown in elevation and plan at Fig. 8·48. The given views are in First Angle Projection. Assume the surfaces to be transparent and draw FULL SIZE the given views. Determine the edge of intersection of the two surfaces, record its true length, and insert its projections on the given views.

239

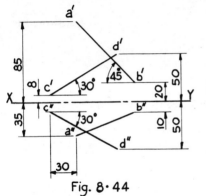

Fig. 8·44

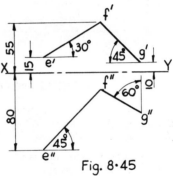

Fig. 8·45

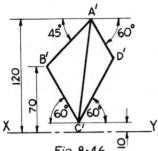

Fig. 8·46

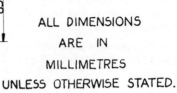

Fig. 8·47

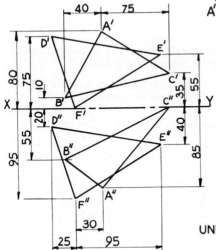

Fig. 8·48

ALL DIMENSIONS
ARE IN
MILLIMETRES
UNLESS OTHERWISE STATED.

MISCELLANEOUS ASSIGNMENTS

1. What is the difference between First, Second, Third and Fourth Angle Orthographic projections? Why are Second and Fourth angle not regarded as standard methods of projection?

2. A right circular cone is illustrated at Fig. 9·1.
Draw the given view and project the true shape of the parabola obtained by cutting the cone by the Section Plane XX.

3. Draw, FULL SIZE, a helix assuming a diameter of 62 mm and a pitch of 75 mm. Give a brief outline of the application of the curve to general engineering practice.

4. (a) When "lining in" a drawing, why is it better to line in curves *before* straight lines?

(b "A drawing prepared for the purpose of manufacturing a component is a Specification." Discuss this statement briefly, illustrating your answer by means of freehand sketches.

5. A cylinder of 62 mm diameter rests on the H.P. with its axis parallel to the H.P. and V.P. A vertical hole of 38 mm diameter is drilled through the cylinder and the axis of the hole is 7 mm in front of the cylinder axis. Draw, FULL SIZE, the plan and elevation of the cylinder showing the curves of intersection.

6. The line Q.P. (Fig. 9·2) is a tangent to a parabola at the point P, and Q lies on the axis of the curve. Assuming a base width of 100 mm, plot the curve FULL SIZE and find the position of the directrix. The line that bisects PQ at 90 degrees passes through the focus of the parabola.

7. A point P which lies on a rectangular hyperbola is 25 mm. from OX and 125 mm from OY (Fig. 9·3). Plot the curve FULL SIZE and draw a tangent through a point on the curve 38 mm from OY. OX and OY are the asymptotes. Plot curve between limits OX=OY=125 mm.

8. If OY and OX are the asymptotes of a hyperbola (Fig. 9·4) and P lies on the curve, plot the curve FULL SIZE between the limits OX=150 mm and OY=112 mm.

9. Use the cone illustrated at Fig. 9·1 and draw, FULL SIZE, the parabola which has a focal sphere 25 mm. diameter.

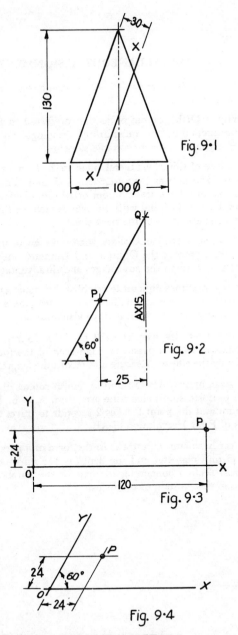

Fig. 9·1

Fig. 9·2

Fig. 9·3

Fig. 9·4

ALL DIMENSIONS ARE IN MILLIMETRES

MISCELLANEOUS ASSIGNMENTS

10. Draw an Isometric view of a standard hexogonal nut M24. Scale: TWICE FULL SIZE.

11. Why is Orthographic projection preferred to Pictorial projection for the production of "manufacturing" drawings?
Illustrate your answer by suitable sketches.

12. A piece of thin sheet metal is cut in the form of an ellipse having a major axis = 150 mm and a minor axis = 75 mm. The elliptical sheet is then bent around a vertical cylinder of 50 mm diameter with the minor axis behind and coinciding with the cylinder axis in the elevation. Draw, FULL SIZE, the elevation of the bent sheet.

13. Draw, FULL SIZE, an Oblique Pictorial view of the nut described in Problem 10. Compare the Oblique and Isometric views of this nut and comment briefly upon the advantages and disadvantages of each.

14. It is sometimes difficult to establish by visualization which are the visible faces on a Second Auxiliary view. Describe a simple method of determination which does not involve visualization.

15. Draw, FULL SIZE, a square ABCD of side 55 mm. An ellipse having a minor axis of 59 mm passes through each of the four points A, B, C and D. Draw the ellipse. Measure and record the length of the major axis.

16. A straight arm AB 150 mm in length rotates about A. A point P moves at uniform speed along the arm from A to B. If the arm rotates at 60 r.p.m. and the point P takes 2 seconds to travel from A to B, plot the locus of P for 1 revolution of AB.

17. A car headlamp reflector is in the form of a paraboloid. The open end is 145 mm diameter and the depth is 175 mm. Draw, FULL SIZE, a longitudinal section containing the axis of the paraboloid and find by construction the position of the focus.

MISCELLANEOUS ASSIGNMENTS

18. A length of 6 mm square section wire is formed into a helical spring by winding it tightly around a mandrel 62 mm diameter. If the pitch of the coils is 25 mm, draw, FULL SIZE, the elevation and end view of the spring; 3 coils only need be drawn. Show all construction lines.

19. When deciding whether to insert or omit hidden detail from orthographic views, what factors should be considered?

20. Sketch freehand:

   (a) A Woodruff Key;

   (b) A Gib-Head Key;

   (c) A Splined Shaft.

(a) and (b) should be sketched pictorially and (c) orthographically, showing an elevation and an end view.

21. Draw two identical equilateral triangles ABC and $A_1B_1C_1$ of 75 mm side so that the first triangle ABC is above $A_1B_1C_1$ and in vertical alignment with it. ABC represents the elevation of a flat surface and $A_1B_1C_1$ is its plan. Find the true shape of the surface (a) by the method used for obtaining the development of surfaces, (b) by auxiliary projection.

22. Discuss briefly either

   (a) Progressive and Chain dimensioning; or

   (b) Implied Limits and Specified Tolerances.

23. Define an Involute.
Draw, FULL SIZE, the involute to a 35 mm diameter circle. One convolution of the curve only is required.

24. A 75 mm diameter circle rolls without slipping around the inside of another circle of 125 mm diameter. Construct the locus of a point P situated 12 mm inside the circumference of the rolling circle during 1 complete revolution. P is assumed to rotate with the rolling circle.

25. An oblique cone of vertical height 90 mm and base diameter 75 mm is hollow and made of thin sheet metal. The axis of the cone is inclined to the base at 60 degrees. Ignoring the base, what is the size of the smallest sheet from which the development of the cone could be cut

1. _ SCREW THREADS:

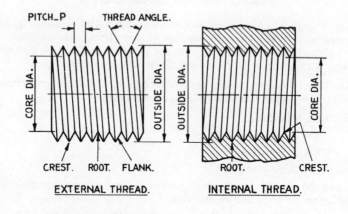

PITCH _ P   THREAD ANGLE.

CORE DIA.   OUTSIDE DIA.

OUTSIDE DIA.   CORE DIA.

CREST.   ROOT.   FLANK.

ROOT.   CREST.

EXTERNAL THREAD.   INTERNAL THREAD.

2 _ I.S.O. METRIC THREAD FORM:

ROUND OR FLAT CREST,
ROUND ROOT.

ROUND OR FLAT ROOT,
FLAT CREST.

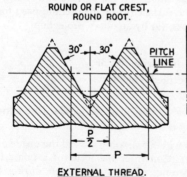
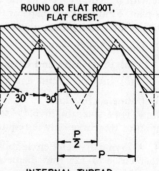

30°   30°   PITCH LINE

$\dfrac{P}{2}$

P

30°   30°

$\dfrac{P}{2}$

P

EXTERNAL THREAD.   INTERNAL THREAD.

3_ POWER TRANSMISSION THREAD FORMS:

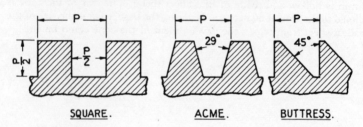

P   P   P

$\dfrac{P}{2}$

$\dfrac{P}{2}$

29°

45°

SQUARE.   ACME.   BUTTRESS.

245

SCREWED FASTENINGS.

I. HEXAGONAL BOLT AND NUT.

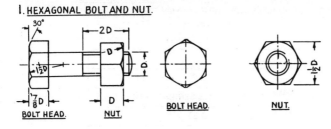

BOLT HEAD. NUT. BOLT HEAD. NUT.

2. STUD AND HEXAGONAL NUT.   ## 3. SCREW. (ROUND HEAD)

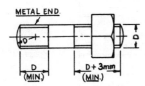 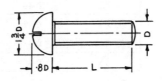

TYPICAL FASTENINGS:-

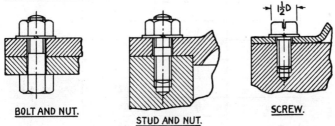

BOLT AND NUT.   STUD AND NUT.   SCREW.

TYPICAL BOLT AND SCREW HEADS:-

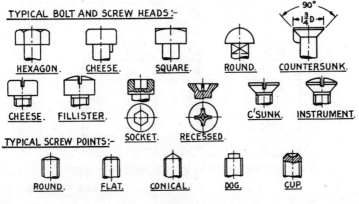

HEXAGON.   CHEESE.   SQUARE.   ROUND.   COUNTERSUNK.

CHEESE.   FILLISTER.   SOCKET.   RECESSED.   C'SUNK.   INSTRUMENT.

TYPICAL SCREW POINTS:-

ROUND.   FLAT.   CONICAL.   DOG.   CUP.

246·

I.S.O. METRIC SCREW THREADS.
SELECTED 'COARSE' AND 'FINE' SERIES FOR SCREWS, BOLTS AND NUTS AND OTHER COMMON THREADED FASTENERS.
DIMENSIONS IN MILLIMETRES.

1	2	3
BASIC MAJOR DIAMETERS.	PITCHES.	
	COARSE SERIES	FINE SERIES.
✳ 1·6	0·35	—
1·8	0·35	—
✳ 2	0·4	—
2·2	0·45	—
✳ 2·5	0·45	—
✳ 3	0·5	—
3·5	0·6	—
✳ 4	0·7	—
4·5	0·75	—
✳ 5	0·8	—
✳ 6	1	—
7	1	—
✳ 8	1·25	1
✳ 10	1·5	1·25
✳ 12	1·75	1·25
14	2	1·5
✳ 16	2	1·5
18	2·5	1·5
✳ 20	2·5	1·5
22	2·5	1·5
✳ 24	3	2
27	3	2
✳ 30	3·5	2
33	3·5	2
✳ 36	4	3
39	4	3

✳ PREFERENCE SHOULD BE GIVEN TO THESE DIAMETERS.

B.S.3643: PT.I.:1963.

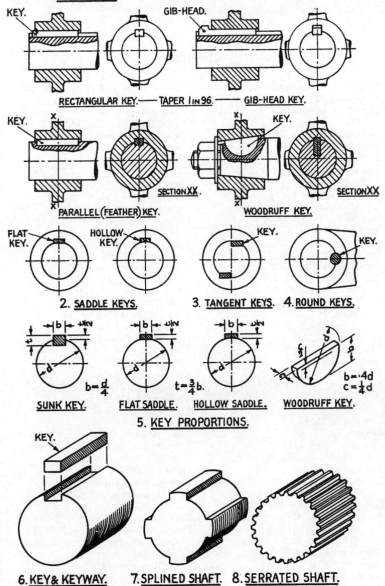

1. SUNK KEYS.

KEY.

GIB-HEAD.

RECTANGULAR KEY. — TAPER 1 IN 96. — GIB-HEAD KEY.

KEY.

KEY.

SECTION XX.

SECTION XX

PARALLEL (FEATHER) KEY.   WOODRUFF KEY.

FLAT KEY.   HOLLOW KEY.   KEY.   KEY.

2. SADDLE KEYS.   3. TANGENT KEYS.   4. ROUND KEYS.

$b = \dfrac{d}{4}$ $t = \dfrac{3}{4}b.$ $b = .4d$
$c = \dfrac{1}{4}d$

SUNK KEY.   FLAT SADDLE.   HOLLOW SADDLE.   WOODRUFF KEY.

5. KEY PROPORTIONS.

KEY.

6. KEY & KEYWAY.   7. SPLINED SHAFT.   8. SERRATED SHAFT.

248

INDEX